MERRILL
LIFE SCIENCE

STUDY GUIDE

GLENCOE
Macmillan/McGraw–Hill

Lake Forest, Illinois   Columbus, Ohio   Mission Hills, California   Peoria, Illinois

A GLENCOE PROGRAM

Merrill Life Science, *Student Edition*

Merrill Life Science, *Teacher Wraparound Edition*

Merrill Life Science, *Teacher Resource Package*

Merrill Life Science, *Study Guide, Student Edition*

Merrill Life Science, *Reinforcement, Student Edition*

Merrill Life Science, *Enrichment, Student Edition*

Merrill Life Science, *Transparency Package*

Merrill Life Science, *Laboratory Manual*

Merrill Life Science, *Laboratory Manual,*
Teacher Annotated Edition

Merrill Life Science, *Spanish Resources*

Merrill Life Science, *Chapter Review Software*

Merrill Life Science, *Computer Test Bank*

Merrill Life Science, *Videodisc Correlation*

TO THE STUDENT

This Study Guide for *Merrill Life Science* provides you with an easy way to learn life science. Each chapter's worksheets closely follow the chapter text and help you understand new vocabulary and major concepts. The chapter's subject matter is well covered as you complete such tasks as fill-in-the-blank, matching, and word scrambles.

Complete the Study Guide as you finish the text reading assignments. You will find the directions are simple and easy to follow.

Send all inquiries to:
Glencoe Publishing Company
936 Eastwind Drive
Westerville, Ohio 43081

Printed in the United States of America

ISBN 0-675-16766-3

2 3 4 5 6 7 8 9 10 99 98 97 96 95 94 93 92

TABLE OF CONTENTS

Table of Contents (continued)

STUDY GUIDE   Chapter 1

Living Things   Text Pages 6–9

*Cross out the statements 1–10 that **DO NOT** agree with the textbook.*

1. The main source of energy for most organisms is the sun.

2. All living things increase in size, or grow.

3. Unlike animals, plants never move.

4. The life span of all living things is about the same.

5. Living things use the same water, oxygen, and minerals that have been used since life began.

6. All organisms are many-celled.

7. Living things are made up of about 70 percent water.

8. Animals use their senses to respond to stimuli.

9. Only animals need energy, because plants do not need to move.

10. All organisms take part in many interacting cycles with one another and with all the nonliving things around them.

11. In the illustration to the right, what is the stimulus that this person is responding to? _____

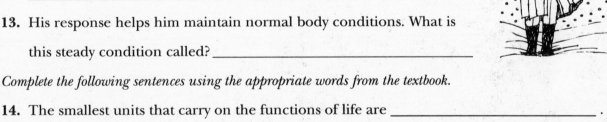

12. What is his response to that stimulus? _____
   _____

13. His response helps him maintain normal body conditions. What is this steady condition called? _____

Complete the following sentences using the appropriate words from the textbook.

14. The smallest units that carry on the functions of life are _____ .

15. The _____ is the length of time an organism is expected to live.

16. Individual living things are called _____ .

17. All the changes living things undergo as they grow are called _____ .

18. An _____ is a characteristic an organism has that makes it better able to survive in its environment.

STUDY GUIDE

Chapter 1

Where Does Life Come From?

Text Pages 10–12

Check (✓) the statements that agree with the textbook.

_____ 1. Life was probably formed from nonliving matter sometime between 4.6 billion and 3.5 billion years ago.

_____ 2. Spallanzani once wrote a recipe for making mice.

_____ 3. Louis Pasteur disproved the theory of biogenesis.

_____ 4. For much of history, people believed that living things came spontaneously from nonliving matter.

_____ 5. The atmosphere of early Earth was made up of gases like ammonia, hydrogen, methane, and water vapor.

_____ 6. Life comes from life.

_____ 7. Francesco Redi proved that maggots come from eggs laid by flies and not from meat.

_____ 8. Scientists think that the planet Earth is about 4.6 million years old.

_____ 9. American Stanley Miller proved that Oparin was right.

_____ 10. Biogenesis is the theory that living things come only from living things.

_____ 11. In the mid-1800s, Louis Pasteur showed that broth was contaminated only when exposed to air.

_____ 12. Alexander Oparin believed that life came from other planets.

_____ 13. Some rocks up to 3.5 million years old contain fossils of once-living organisms.

_____ 14. Spallanzani destroyed maggots by boiling water.

_____ 15. Oparin believed that lightning and ultraviolet rays helped early gases combine.

Each illustration represents a theory of where life comes from. Label each with the name of the theory it represents.

16. _____   17. _____

STUDY GUIDE

What Is Science?

Write the letter of the term or phrase that best completes each sentence.

_____ 1. A _____ is what is being tested in an experiment.
   a. variable   **b.** control

_____ 2. A scientific _____ tells how nature works.
   a. hypothesis   **b.** law

_____ 3. The standard used to compare the test materials is the _____ .
   a. variable   **b.** control

_____ 4. An explanation of things or events based on many observations is a _____ .
   a. theory   **b.** method

_____ 5. A _____ is a prediction that can be tested.
   a. conclusion   **b.** hypothesis

The words and phrases that follow are steps in a scientific method. Rewrite them in the correct order.

form a hypothesis   gather information
reach a conclusion   experiment
observe   accept or reject the hypothesis
do something with the results

6. _____

7. _____

8. _____

9. _____

10. _____

11. _____

12. _____

Match the prefix to the meaning by writing the correct letter in each blank.

_____ 13. kilo-   **a.** 0.01

_____ 14. centi-   **b.** 1000.0

_____ 15. milli-   **c.** 0.001

STUDY GUIDE

The Impact of Science on Your Life

*Cross out the statements that **DO NOT** agree with the textbook.*

1. Most water systems are now fluoridated and tooth decay has decreased.

2. You may have a greater chance of developing cancer than your ancestors did 100 years ago.

3. Technology is beneficial in every way.

4. Penicillin is used to fluoridate the water.

5. In many countries, about 50 percent of infants die due to contaminated water and milk.

6. Global warming is causing cancer in greater numbers than before.

7. Today, milk contains dangerous microorganisms due to pasteurization.

8. Technology is using scientific knowledge to solve everyday problems.

9. Many great advances have also come with many problems.

10. People benefit from science economically, nutritionally, medically, and environmentally.

11. Pesticides, food preservatives, and artificial sweeteners may have contributed to the increased incidence of cancer.

12. Many diseases are acquired from penicillin, fluoridated water, and irradiated foods.

13. Global warming may change the temperature of Earth.

14. Technology has unforeseen side effects.

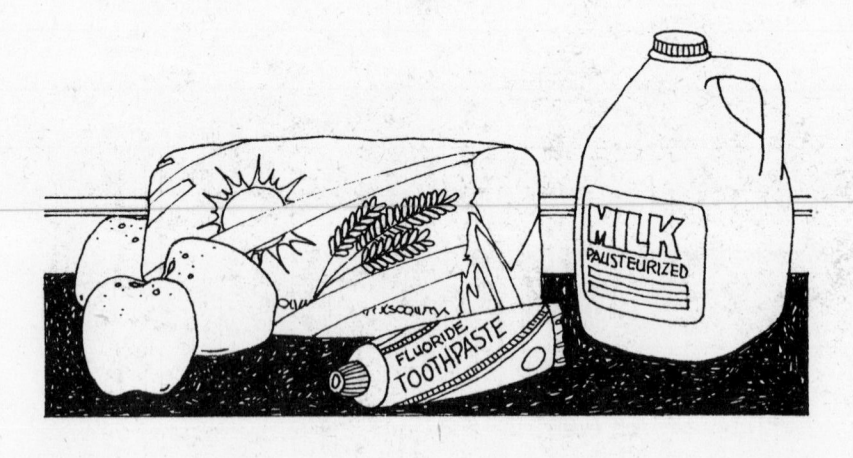

STUDY GUIDE

Chapter 2

Cells: The Units of Life

Text Pages 30–35

Complete the following sentences using appropriate terms from the textbook.

1. A light microscope having two lenses is called a _____ .

2. If the eyepiece lens of a microscope has a power of 10× and the objective lens has a power of 43×, then the _____ is 430×.

3. Instead of a standard lens, the electron microscope uses a _____ to bend electrons.

4. The surfaces of whole objects can be examined with a _____ electron microscope.

5. If your class wanted to have a better look at an earthworm, a _____ light microscope could be used.

6. A _____ is used to see what is inside of a cell.

7. The _____ states that organisms are made of cells, cells are the basic units of structure and function in organisms, and cells come from preexisting cells.

8. A _____ microscope lets light pass through an object and then through two or more lenses.

9. The eyepiece lens usually has a power of _____ .

10. SEM stands for _____ .

11. The first person to use the term "cell" was looking through a microscope at a slice of _____ .

12. Before the discovery that cells _____ to form new cells, people thought life occurred spontaneously.

13. A magnifying glass works like a _____ microscope because it has only one lens.

14. In a light microscope, the lenses _____ the image and _____ light toward your eye.

Match the statement on the left with the person on the right.

_____ 15. observed that every cell comes from a cell that existed before

_____ 16. made the first compound microscope

_____ 17. concluded that all animals are made up of cells

_____ 18. called boxlike structures in cork "cells"

_____ 19. made a simple microscope with a glass bead

a. Rudolph Virchow

b. Anton Van Leeuwenhoek

c. Zacharias Janssen

d. Theodor Schwann

e. Robert Hooke

STUDY GUIDE

Chapter 2

Cell Structure

Text Pages 36–43

In the blank at the left, write the letter of the word or phrase that best completes the sentence.

_____ 1. Cells make their own protein on round structures called _____ .
 a. Golgi bodies **b.** mitochondria **c.** ribosomes **d.** lysosomes

_____ 2. Mitochondria supply the cell with _____ .
 a. oxygen **b.** nutrients **c.** energy **d.** enzymes

_____ 3. Plants can trap light energy in organelles called _____ .
 a. vacuoles **b.** cell walls **c.** mitochondria **d.** chloroplasts

_____ 4. Golgi bodies can be compared to _____ in a bakery.
 a. loading docks **b.** power plants **c.** warehouses **d.** managers

_____ 5. Plant cells differ from animal cells because plant cells have _____ .
 a. cell membranes **c.** nuclear membranes
 b. cell walls **d.** endoplasmic reticulum

_____ 6. Prokaryotic cells do not have any _____ .
 a. cytoplasm **c.** organelles
 b. DNA **d.** membrane-covered organelles

_____ 7. Muscle cells have large numbers of _____ .
 a. chromosomes **b.** mitochondria **c.** chloroplasts **d.** cellulose fibers

_____ 8. Vacuoles may store _____ .
 a. waste products **b.** oxygen **c.** energy **d.** pigment

_____ 9. Plants can change light energy into chemical energy in the form of _____ .
 a. protein **b.** fat **c.** sugar **d.** fiber

_____ 10. Chromatin is made up of _____ .
 a. ATP **b.** chlorophyll **c.** DNA **d.** spores

In the blank at the left, write the letter of the term that best matches the phrase.

_____ 11. made of double layer of fats **a.** cytoplasm

_____ 12. directs the cell's activities **b.** endoplasmic reticulum

_____ 13. gel-like material inside cells **c.** Golgi bodies

_____ 14. folded membranes that move materials in cells **d.** cell membrane

_____ 15. package and move proteins **e.** lysosome

_____ 16. digests wastes **f.** nucleus

_____ 17. storage areas **g.** vacuoles

STUDY GUIDE

Cell Organization

Check (✔) the statements that agree with the textbook. Rewrite the statements that disagree.

_____ **1.** A human egg cell is about ten times bigger than a human red blood cell.

_____ **2.** Hollow cells in plant stems transport food and water.

_____ **3.** Human red blood cells have long extensions.

_____ **4.** The cells in a tissue do different sorts of work.

_____ **5.** Different types of tissues in an organ work together.

_____ **6.** An organ system is a group of organisms working together.

_____ **7.** Your heart is an organ.

_____ **8.** Some cells can change shape.

_____ **9.** A whole plant is an organism.

_____ **10.** Your heart and blood vessels work together as an organ system.

_____ **11.** In a many-celled organism, each cell works alone.

_____ **12.** All cells are about the same size.

_____ **13.** An organ is made up of different types of tissues.

Complete the following sentences using appropriate terms from the textbook.

14. Many organ systems working together make up an _____ .

15. The leaf of a plant is an _____ .

16. Groups of similar cells that do the same sort of work are called _____ .

17. _____ have fine extensions.

18. Human red blood cells are _____ -shaped.

19. The roots, stems, and leaves of a plant are called _____ .

20. A single nerve cell can be as long as _____ .

21. Different types of _____ work together to make up an organ.

22. The _____ of a cell tells you something about its function.

23. The leaf functions as an organ to make _____ for the plant.

STUDY GUIDE

Chapter 2

Organ Transplants

Text Pages 46–47

Complete the following sentences using appropriate terms from the textbook.

1. A baboon _____ was transplanted into an infant in 1984.

2. When the immune system successfully attacks a new organ, the organ undergoes

   _____ .

3. As in blood transfusions, a donor organ must _____ a recipient's tissue type.

4. The _____ often attacks a transplanted organ.

5. A drug called _____ has helped prevent rejection of transplanted organs.

6. Scientists may someday be able to grow new organs in the laboratory using organ

   _____ .

7. Someday, animals might be raised specifically for organ _____ into humans.

8. An example of an organ that is often transplanted in humans is the

   _____ .

9. The human immune system usually fights _____ .

10. Scientists have successfully constructed a _____ for a dog using

    _____ taken from the dog's back.

Match the statements with the proper terms.

_____ 11. person receiving transplanted organ

_____ 12. problem resulting when donor and recipient organ types don't match

_____ 13. constructed from the back muscles of dogs

_____ 14. person giving organ for transplant

_____ 15. transplanted organs seen as this during rejection

_____ 16. turns down the immune system

_____ 17. can be grown from tissue samples

_____ 18. normally attacked by the immune system

a. donor

b. immune system

c. rejection

d. heart

e. recipient

f. foreign invader

g. cyclosporine

h. organs

i. viruses

STUDY GUIDE

Chapter 3

Chemistry of Living Things

Text Pages 54–57

Match the correct term with the phrase.

_____ **1.** anything that has mass and takes up space

_____ **2.** the ability to do work

_____ **3.** small particles that are the basic units of matter

_____ **4.** contains protons and neutrons

_____ **5.** particles that move around the outside of the nucleus

_____ **6.** a substance made of only one type of atom

_____ **7.** two or more elements chemically combined

_____ **8.** the smallest part of a compound having all the properties of that compound

a. nucleus of an atom

b. element

c. molecule

d. matter

e. compound

f. electrons

g. energy

h. atoms

Check the (✓) statements that agree with the textbook. Rewrite the statements that disagree.

_____ **1.** Compounds that contain carbon are organic.

_____ **2.** Most substances will not dissolve in water.

_____ **3.** Blood is a suspension.

_____ **4.** Substances in a mixture lose their original properties.

_____ **5.** Glucose is a compound used by the body for energy.

_____ **6.** Water is one of the most important compounds in living things.

_____ **7.** Nucleic acids break down the food we eat into a usable form.

_____ **8.** Sugar, starch, and cellulose are all carbohydrates.

_____ **9.** DNA and RNA are nucleic acids.

_____ **10.** An element can be broken down into simpler forms.

_____ **11.** A proton is a particle with a positive charge.

_____ **12.** The total electrical charge of an atom is one.

_____ **13.** Proteins are made up of amino acids.

_____ **14.** Two or more elements that are joined chemically are called a solution.

_____ **15.** Lipids can store energy.

_____ **16.** Nucleic acids are inorganic.

_____ **17.** Enzymes are changed during a chemical reaction.

STUDY GUIDE

Cell Transport

Write the letter of the term that best completes each sentence.

_____ 1. The passage of large molecules through the cell membrane into the cell is called _____ .
   a. endocytosis   c. passive transport
   b. exocytosis   d. osmosis

_____ 2. Active transport always requires _____ .
   a. water   c. equilibrium
   b. energy   d. osmosis

_____ 3. The movement of molecules from an area where there are many to where there are few is called _____ .
   a. diffusion   b. equilibrium   c. homeostasis   d. transport

Check (✔) the statements that agree with the textbook. Rewrite the statements that disagree.

_____ 1. The cell uses energy to transport glucose through the cell membrane.

_____ 2. Proteins are transported by the Golgi bodies.

_____ 3. Diffusion is a type of active transport.

_____ 4. The cell membrane is permeable to proteins.

_____ 5. No energy is required for the movement of water molecules across the cell membrane.

_____ 6. Osmosis is a type of passive transport involving elements such as calcium.

_____ 7. Elements such as sodium and potassium diffuse through the cell membrane.

_____ 8. Carrier proteins are located in the cell membrane.

_____ 9. Random movement of molecules stops once equilibrium is reached.

_____ 10. Molecules tend to move into areas where there are more molecules.

Study the diagram below and answer the questions that follow.

a.   b.   c.

1. What process is taking place from diagram a to diagram c? _____

2. What state has been reached in diagram c? _____

3. Does this process require energy? _____

STUDY GUIDE

Energy in Cells

Complete the following sentences using appropriate terms from the textbook.

1. Plants get their energy from the _____ .

2. The green pigment in plants is called _____ .

3. Organisms that can make their own food are called _____ .

4. A food chain always begins with a _____ .

5. The process by which plants change light energy into chemical energy is called

   _____ .

6. All the chemical changes that occur within the cells of an organism is called

   _____ .

7. During fermentation, _____ and _____
   are produced.

8. Overworked muscles can still produce energy when oxygen levels are low by the process of

   _____ .

9. The metabolism of glucose when oxygen is present is called _____ .

10. Consumers obtain energy by eating _____ and other consumers.

Write the letter of the term that best matches each phrase.

_____ 1. energy is given off in the absence of oxygen	**a.**	glucose
_____ 2. energy source necessary for photosynthesis	**b.**	chlorophyll
_____ 3. causes muscles to tire	**c.**	mitochondria
_____ 4. made and stored by plants	**d.**	sunlight
_____ 5. obtain energy from producers	**e.**	oxygen
_____ 6. traps radiant energy	**f.**	consumers
_____ 7. energy can be lost in this form	**g.**	alcohol
_____ 8. contain green pigment	**h.**	chloroplasts
_____ 9. place where glucose is metabolized	**i.**	water
_____ 10. combines with glucose during respiration	**j.**	heat
_____ 11. fermentation product in yeast	**k.**	fermentation
_____ 12. waste product in respiration	**l.**	lactic acid

STUDY GUIDE   Chapter 3

Nonbiodegradable Materials in Your Environment!   Text Pages 66–67

Put the following items in the recycling truck or in the compost heap where they will decompose. Write the letter of the item on the line in the diagram.

a. motor oil

b. aluminum cans

c. leaves

d. tin cans

e. fruit

f. glass bottles

g. plastic bags

h. newspapers

Complete the following sentences using appropriate terms from the textbook.

1. When something can be used over and over again, we say that it can be _____,

2. When substances break down easily in the environment by living things, they are said to be

   _____ .

3. Name two of the factors that help substances to break down naturally. _____

   _____

4. Another way of saying that a substance can "break down" is to say that it can._____

5. Plants return _____ to the soil when they break down.

6. How long does it take for a tin can to break down in the environment? _____

7. Give some examples of biodegradable materials. _____

   _____

8. Give some examples of nonbiodegradable materials. _____

   _____

9. What is the best way to control the use of nonbiodegradable products? _____

   _____

10. Why are nonbiodegradable items a problem in our world? _____

    _____

NAME _____ DATE _____ CLASS _____

Cell Growth and Division

Write the name of the phase of the cell cycle next to each event described below.

_____ 1. centromeres divide

_____ 2. centrioles move to opposite ends of the cell

_____ 3. nuclear membrane forms around each mass of chromosomes

_____ 4. chromosome strands separate toward opposite ends of the cell

_____ 5. a copy of each chromosome is made

_____ 6. centromeres attach to the spindle fibers

_____ 7. the nuclear membrane disappears

_____ 8. the material in the nucleus that appears grainy condenses to become visible as chromosomes

_____ 9. double-stranded chromosomes line up in the center of the cell

_____ 10. chromatin condenses and becomes visible

Complete the following sentences using appropriate words from the textbook.

11. In animal cells, once the nucleus has divided, the _____ pinches in to form two new cells.

12. Cell division resulting in two new nuclei having the same number of chromosomes as the original nucleus is called _____ .

13. Eggs or sperm are _____ cells.

14. Plant cells have no _____ .

15. Plant and animal cells have _____ fibers during mitosis.

16. Bacteria reproduce asexually by means of a process called _____ .

17. In plant cells, a structure called a _____ forms between two new nuclei.

18. The process by which a new organism is produced when sex cells from two parents combine is called _____ .

19. Budding is a form of _____ .

20. A whole new organism can grow from just a piece of the parent in animals that have the ability to _____ .

STUDY GUIDE   Chapter 4

Sexual Reproduction and Meiosis   Text Pages 82–85

Place a check (✔) next to the sentences that agree with the textbook. Rewrite the sentences that disagree.

_____ 1. The egg and sperm have a diploid chromosome number.

_____ 2. The chromosome number is reduced by a process called mitosis.

_____ 3. When two gametes join, the chromosome number is doubled.

_____ 4. The fusion of an egg and sperm is called meiosis.

_____ 5. Body cells contain pairs of chromosomes.

_____ 6. A zygote has a diploid chromosome number.

_____ 7. Meiosis produces cells with a diploid chromosome number.

_____ 8. After two nuclear divisions in meiosis, four cells result.

_____ 9. Gametes contain only one chromosome from each matched pair.

_____ 10. Meiosis can occur anywhere in the body.

Label the following diagram using these terms: spindle fiber, double-stranded chromosome, centromere, centriole.

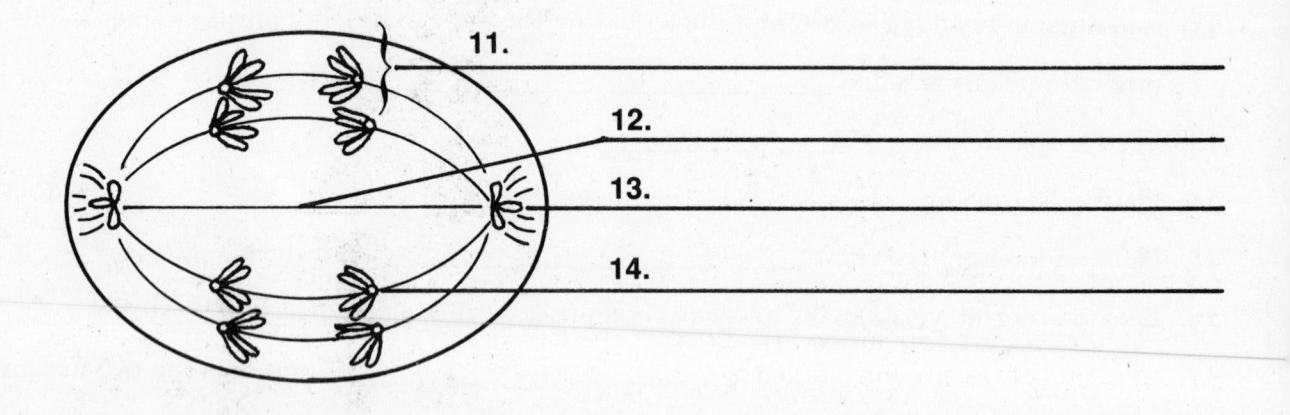

11. _____

12. _____

13. _____

14. _____

STUDY GUIDE

Chapter 4

DNA

Text Pages 86–91

Match the statements on the left with the terms on the right by writing the correct letter in the space provided.

_____ 1. units that make up proteins

_____ 2. used to demonstrate that the DNA molecule is a helix

_____ 3. where messenger RNA attaches during protein construction

_____ 4. pairs with cytosine

_____ 5. sugar molecules in DNA

_____ 6. the part of DNA that directs the making of a specific protein

_____ 7. hypothesized that nitrogen bases in DNA occur in pairs

_____ 8. used to build cells and tissues

_____ 9. made a working model of the DNA molecule

_____ 10. contains uracil

a. deoxyribose

b. ribosomes

c. amino acids

d. X rays

e. Watson and Crick

f. Chargaff

g. RNA

h. protein

i. gene

j. guanine

Complete the following sentences using the appropriate words from the textbook.

11. The process by which DNA copies itself is called _____ .

12. Hair color and freckles are both _____ .

13. During the making of a protein, amino acids are brought to the ribosome

   by _____ .

14. The "handrails" of each DNA strand are made up of _____ and

   _____ .

15. Any permanent change in the genetic material of a cell is called a _____ .

16. DNA strands held together by _____ are separated by

   an _____ during replication.

17. Changes in the order of amino acids will change the _____ produced.

18. _____ carries the code for amino acids.

19. The basic units of inheritance are _____ .

20. The shape of a DNA molecule is a _____ .

STUDY GUIDE

Inventing Organisms

Fill in the blanks with the appropriate terms from the textbook.

1. Insertion of a specific human gene into a mouse resulted in the mouse having a greater chance of getting _____ .

2. A government-issued license to control the manufacture and sale of an invention is called a _____ .

3. Many people are opposed to having legal _____ over living organisms.

4. Some scientists see the patent as a barrier to _____ new findings within the scientific community.

5. In 1988, the United States government gave the first transgenic organism patent to _____ .

6. Organisms that contain genetic information from another species are called _____ .

7. _____ drugs can be tested in transgenic mice.

8. A gene from _____ can be transplanted into crops to prevent some insect damage.

9. Some people worry that genetically engineered animals and plants might displace or destroy _____ species.

10. The technology used to produce transgenic organisms is called _____ .

STUDY GUIDE

What Is Genetics?

For each item, cross out the phrase or phrases that do not accurately complete the statement.

1. Genes
   a. are made up of DNA.
   b. control the traits that show up in an organism.
   c. are found on chromosomes.
   d. are never inherited by some people.
   e. have different forms called alleles.

2. Gregor Mendel
   a. is the Father of Genetics.
   b. lived in Europe in the 1800s.
   c. experimented with peas.
   d. arrived at his conclusions by accident.
   e. determined the basic laws of genetics.
   f. changed the thinking of the scientists of his day.

3. Alleles
   a. are forms of a gene.
   b. are the subject of genetics.
   c. can be dominant or recessive.
   d. for a trait from both parents are found in one gamete.

4. A Punnett square
   a. is used to predict results in genetics.
   b. represents the genotypes of offspring that can result from the combination of alleles from two parents.
   c. uses numbers to represent the offspring of two or more parents.

5. A genotype of an organism
   a. is a physical trait.
   b. is its genetic makeup.
   c. determines its phenotype.

6. A recessive factor
   a. can seem to disappear in a generation of organisms.
   b. is represented by a capital letter on a Punnett square.
   c. covers, or dominates, a dominant factor.

7. An organism that is heterozygous for a trait
   a. has two different alleles for that trait.
   b. is a purebred.
   c. has the phenotype of the recessive allele.

STUDY GUIDE

Genetics Since Mendel

Write the letter of the term or phrase that best completes the sentence.

_____ 1. When both alleles of a gene are expressed in the offspring, the condition is called _____ .
    a. heredity   **c.** blending
    b. mixing   **d.** incomplete dominance

_____ 2. An example of incomplete dominance is _____ .
    a. a white allele and a red allele in a plant producing pink flowers
    b. red flowers crossed with white flowers producing both red and white flowers
    c. a red allele covering a white allele in red flowers
    d. a dominant pink allele covering recessive red and white alleles

_____ 3. Because alleles A and B for blood type are inherited by incomplete dominance, a person with genotype AB would have the phenotype _____ .
    a. A   **c.** AB
    b. B   **d.** O

_____ 4. Because the alleles A and B are both dominant and the O allele is recessive, a person with phenotype O would have genotype _____ .
    a. AO   **c.** ABO
    b. BO   **d.** OO

_____ 5. A person with phenotype A blood could not be the parent of an offspring with phenotype _____ blood.
    a. O   **c.** AB
    b. A   **d.** B

For each item, identify the type of inheritance. Write "multiple allele" or "polygenic" in the blank.

_____ 6. A group of genes acts together to produce a single trait.

_____ 7. One trait is controlled by more than two alleles of a gene.

_____ 8. There are three alleles for human blood type.

_____ 9. Up to six gene pairs may control the color of human skin.

_____ 10. The effect of a single allele may be small, but the combination of alleles from many genes produces a wide variety in a trait.

_____ 11. Human traits such as eye and hair color, height, and weight are controlled by two or more gene pairs.

STUDY GUIDE

Human Genetics

Complete the following sentences using the appropriate words from the textbook.

1. Some _____ , or alterations in DNA, have resulted in genetic disorders.

2. The inherited disease in which red blood cells are sickle-shaped instead of disc-shaped is called

   _____ .

3. Sickle cells cannot release enough _____ for the body.

4. In cystic fibrosis, a thick _____ affects the lungs and digestive system.

5. The disease in which blood does not clot properly and puts the affected person in danger of

   bleeding to death from even a small scrape is called _____ .

6. A heterozygous individual who has one allele for a disease but is not affected by it is

   a _____ .

7. Scientists use a chart called a _____ to study the inheritance pattern of a trait.

8. The branch of science in which scientists change genes is called _____ .

Write the letter of the term or phrase that completes the sentence.

_____ 9. Sickle-cell anemia and cystic fibrosis are caused by _____ alleles.
   a. recessive   **b.** dominant

_____ 10. A person who is heterozygous for a disorder caused by a homozygous recessive allele combination _____ affected by the disorder.
   a. will be   **b.** will not be

_____ 11. In order to be affected by hemophilia or color blindness, a male must inherit _____ for the disease.
   a. one allele   **b.** two alleles

_____ 12. In order to be affected by hemophilia or color blindness, a female must inherit _____ for the disease.
   a. one allele   **b.** two alleles

_____ 13. Males are affected by sex-linked genetic disorders _____ than females.
   a. more often   **b.** less often

_____ 14. A male has _____ in his cells.
   a. an X and a Y chromosome
   b. two X chromosomes

_____ 15. A female has _____ in her cells.
   a. an X and a Y chromosome
   b. two X chromosomes

STUDY GUIDE

Chapter 5

The Human Genome

Text Pages 122–123

Answer the following questions using information from the textbook.

1. Where are genes located? _____

2. What does a chromosome map show? _____

3. What is another name for the entire chromosome map of an organism? _____

4. Do scientists know the location of all the genes? _____

5. How many chromosomes are there in each human body cell? _____

6. About how many human genes are there? _____

7. What is the human genome initiative? _____

   _____

8. What are genes made up of? _____

9. What kind of diseases might scientists be able to detect by examining a person's genes?

   _____

10. What benefit is there in knowing that a person may develop a disease? _____

    _____

11. Why might a person make a decision not to have children based on information in the

    genome? _____

    _____

12. What kind of discrimination might a person face whose genome indicates the possibility of the

    development of a certain disease? _____

    _____

    _____

13. How might early detection of a physical or mental handicap benefit a child? _____

    _____

14. How might the human genome initiative benefit other sciences? _____

    _____

15. What benefit is there in knowing the location and DNA code of disease-causing genes?

    _____

    _____

STUDY GUIDE

Mechanisms of Evolution

Use the clues to complete the puzzle.

Across

4. change in the inherited features of an organism over time

6. survival of individuals with the most adapted traits, _____ selection

8. appearance of an inherited trait that makes an individual different from other members of the same species

Down

1. species rapidly evolving due to changes in a few genes, punctuated _____

2. a group of organisms whose members look similar and successfully reproduce among themselves

3. a group of organisms of one species that lives in an area

5. a slow change of one species to another new species

7. developed the theory of evolution by natural selection

STUDY GUIDE

Evidence for Evolution

Complete the statements below using terms from your textbook.

1. Elements whose atoms give off radiation are called _____.

2. A body part which is reduced in size and seems to have no function is called

   a _____.

3. Body parts that are similar in their origin and structure are called _____.

4. Remains of life from an earlier time are called _____.

5. The method of dating fossils by their position in rock layers is

   called _____.

6. The study of the development of embryos is called _____.

7. The type of rock formed by fine particles, such as mud and sand, that contains many fossils

   is _____.

Look at the drawing of layers of rock. Each letter stands for a fossil find. Answer the following questions about the drawing.

8. Which fossil, the one at point *A* or point *B*, is older? Explain your answer.

   _____

   _____

9. Which fossil, the one at point *A* or point *D*, is older? Explain your answer. _____

   _____

   _____

10. Compare the relative ages of fossils found at point *A* and point *C*. Explain your answer.

   _____

STUDY GUIDE

Plant and Animal Extinction

Answer the following questions.

1. What does the word "extinction" mean? _____

2. How does extinction occur? _____

   _____

3. How have humans caused the extinction of some species? _____

   _____

   _____

4. What is an endangered species? _____

   _____

5. How are zoos helpful for endangered species? _____

   _____

6. Explain what is meant by in vitro fertilization and embryo transfer. _____

   _____

   _____

   _____

7. Many medicines are developed from plants. Some of these plants are very rare, growing in only one isolated part of the world. What would happen if these plants became extinct?

   _____

   _____

8. Describe two ways in which we can work to save endangered species.

   _____

   _____

STUDY GUIDE

Chapter 6

Human Evolution

Text Pages 146–149

Match the description in the first column with the item in the second column by writing the correct letter in the space provided.

_____ 1. humanlike primate

_____ 2. human ancestors that lived in South Africa, had a small brain, and walked upright

_____ 3. used stone tools, had a small chin and a large brain, died out about 35 000 years ago

_____ 4. animals with opposable thumbs

_____ 5. "wise human"

_____ 6. lived in caves and looked like modern humans

_____ 7. used stone tools and lived about 1.5 to 2 million years ago

a. *Homo sapiens* Cro-Magnon

b. mammals

c. *Homo sapiens*

d. hominid

e. *Australopithecus*

f. *Homo sapiens* Neanderthal

g. *Homo habilis*

h. primates

Fill in the blanks below with the appropriate terms from the textbook.

8. Monkeys, apes, and humans belong to the group of mammals called

_____ .

9. Primates have _____ that allow them to reach out and bring food to their mouths.

10. Primates have _____ that allows them to judge depth and distance with the eyes.

11. Primates have _____ and _____ that allow them to swing on branches or jungle gyms easily.

12. The _____ of chimpanzees, gorillas, and humans is very similar.

13. The name _____ means southern ape.

14. The name _____ means handyman.

15. _____ humans and _____ humans were early *Homo sapiens*.

16. Neanderthal humans lived in _____ groups.

17. The oldest recorded art was painted on cave walls by _____ humans.

STUDY GUIDE

What Is Classification?

Classifying

Fill in the blanks with the correct terms listed below.

study   communicate   similar   kingdoms   classify   taxonomy   groups

Classifying, or organizing living things into groups, is one way to _____

and _____ about organisms. To _____ means to

organize things into _____ . The groups are based on the ways in which

things are _____ . The science of classifying living things is

called _____ . Aristotle began his system of taxonomy by dividing

organisms into two large _____ .

Scientific Naming

Fill in the blanks with the correct terms listed below. One term will be used twice.

species	scientific name	Panthera	genus
Carolus Linnaeus	Latin	names	bionomial nomenclature
organism	scientific name	two parts	leo

Organisms can have several common or popular _____ . It might be

hard to identify a(n) _____ if it has several names. To avoid this problem,

scientists use a system that gives all organisms a(n) _____ .

For example, the _____ for a lion is *Panthera leo*.

_____ is the genus name for large cats, and lions belong to the

species _____ . The language used for naming organisms is

_____ .

The system for giving organisms a scientific name was first developed by

_____ . His two-word naming system is called

_____ . The first part of the name is the

_____ ; it is always capitalized. The last part of the name is

the _____ ; it starts with a small letter.

STUDY GUIDE

Chapter 7

Modern Classification

Text Pages 160–163

Complete the following sentences using information from the textbook.

1. The kingdom _____ is made up of bacteria and cyanobacteria, single-celled plantlike organisms.

2. The _____ of an organism is its evolutionary history.

3. Monerans are called _____ because they do not have an organized nucleus.

4. A characteristic of the members of the plant kingdom is _____ .

5. Can there be more than one species in a genus? _____

6. The word eukaryote means _____ .

7. The first characteristic to consider when classifying an organism by kingdom, is whether or not the cells have a _____ .

8. The first cells to form on Earth were in the kingdom _____ .

Use the clues below to complete the puzzle.

Across

1. an organism's evolutionary history
5. names a specific organism
6. divides the class Insecta into more than one part
8. classification that divides a phylum
9. created a system to classify organisms

Down

1. "before nucleus"
2. a group within a family
3. the two-word naming system, binomial _____
4. replaces phylum in the plant kingdom
7. classification that divides orders

STUDY GUIDE   Chapter 7

The Rain Forest Crisis   Text Pages 164–165

Fill in the blanks using the correct words below.

species diversity	thirty	extinction	farming	soils
desert	atmosphere	deforestation	rain forests	fifty
carbon dioxide	oxygen	logging		

1. Each minute we lose about _____ more acres

   of _____ .

2. The great variety of plants and animals found in the rain forest is called

   _____ .

3. The destruction of forests is called _____ .

4. We may lose one-fourth of all species in the next _____ years.

5. South Americans need land for _____ and _____ .

6. Climatic changes could result from a damaged _____ .

7. Trees and plants remove _____ from the air.

8. Rain forests typically have poor _____ .

9. With extensive loss of the rain forests, the southeastern United States may become

   a _____ .

10. Deforestation may result in _____ of many species.

Place a check (✔) next to the statements that agree with the textbook. Rewrite the statements that disagree.

_____ 1. There is no place on Earth that has not been touched by human technology.

_____ 2. There are thousands of species of plants and animals yet to be discovered and named.

_____ 3. The rain forests produce carbon dioxide, which is important for the air we breathe.

_____ 4. Once a section of rain forest is cleared, it can be farmed over and over again.

_____ 5. Organisms that haven't even been discovered yet may become extinct if deforestation
continues.

_____ 6. Scientists think that only 15 percent of all the species of plants and animals in the tropical
rain forest have been identified.

_____ 7. The evolution of species from a single ancestor is called species diversity.

_____ 8. Deforestation could add to the carbon dioxide in the atmosphere because plants and
trees remove carbon dioxide.

STUDY GUIDE

Chapter 7

Identifying Organisms

Text Pages 166–169

Place a check (✓) next to the statements that agree with the textbook. Rewrite the statements that disagree.

_____ 1. Animals with the same common name can actually be members of different species.

_____ 2. Scientists use common names to avoid confusion and error.

_____ 3. Organisms with similar evolutionary history are classified separately.

_____ 4. The scientific name gives descriptive information about the species.

_____ 5. A dichotomous key is divided into steps, having two choices at each step.

_____ 6. *Turdus migratorius* is the scientific name for the Australian robin.

Just for fun, see if you can identify yourself using a dichotomous key. Then identify a friend.
1a. If you are female go to step 2.
1b. If you are male go to step 5.
2a. If you have brown or black hair go to step 3.
2b. If you have blonde or red hair go to step 4.
3a. If you have blue, grey, or hazel eyes your name is: _____

3b. If you have brown eyes your name is: _____

4a. If you have blue, grey, or hazel eyes your name is: _____

4b. If you have brown eyes your name is: _____

5a. If you have brown or black hair go to step 6.
5b. If you have blonde or red hair go to step 7.
6a. If you have blue, grey, or hazel eyes your name is: _____

6b. If you have brown eyes your name is: _____

7a. If you have blue, grey, or hazel eyes your name is: _____

7b. If you have brown eyes your name is: _____

Answer the following questions.

1. Would many other people in your classroom fit into the same category as you?_____

2. List some characteristics that you might use to make a more complete dichotomous key.

_____

_____

_____

STUDY GUIDE

Viruses: Are They Alive?

Check (✔) the statements that agree with the textbook.

_____ **1.** A parasite may harm the organism on which it depends.

_____ **2.** Some animal and plant viruses are able to change normal cells into cancerous cells.

_____ **3.** Viruses are classified as members of the Kingdom Monera.

_____ **4.** Edward Jenner developed the first vaccine.

_____ **5.** All viruses contain DNA.

_____ **6.** The shape of all viruses is spherical like a basketball.

_____ **7.** The core of a virus is surrounded by a protein coat.

_____ **8.** Latent viruses can hide inside host cells for a long time.

_____ **9.** Viruses cause disease in protists, fungi, bacteria, plants, and animals.

_____ **10.** Gene therapy involves the transfer of RNA.

_____ **11.** Viruses can be seen by using an ordinary compound microscope.

_____ **12.** A virus can reproduce without a host cell.

_____ **13.** Interferon is produced in animal cells.

_____ **14.** The protein coat of a virus gives the particle its shape.

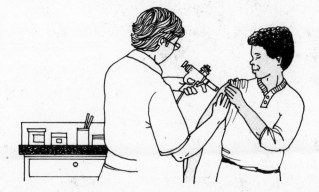

15. The shot being given by the doctor in the illustration will prevent a viral disease. What is the solution in the shot called? _____

16. What is the solution made of? _____

_____

Name the four steps an active virus takes to reproduce itself inside a bacterial cell.

17. _____   **19.** _____

18. _____   **20.** _____

STUDY GUIDE

The Cost of Curing a Disease

*Cross out the statements that **DO NOT** agree with the textbook.*

1. AIDS can be spread through casual contact.

2. The AIDS virus attacks certain white blood cells in the body.

3. The AIDS virus disables the body's immune system.

4. Estimates are that by the year 2000 about 400 people will die from AIDS each year in the United States.

5. The AIDS virus kills by attacking the body's red blood cells.

6. Secondary infections in people with AIDS include pneumonia and tuberculosis.

7. The AIDS virus is spread in body fluids.

8. Drug users get AIDS from the drugs they take.

9. Most people get AIDS through sexual contact.

10. The drug AZT seems to slow down the AIDS infection.

11. Signs of the AIDS virus appear within days after infection.

12. AIDS stands for acquired immune disease syndrome.

Write the common abbreviation for each term in the space provided.

_____ 13. ribonucleic acid; genetic material in some viruses

_____ 14. acquired immune deficiency syndrome; an incurable disease

_____ 15. tuberculosis; a secondary infection

_____ 16. zidovudine; drug used to treat a viral disease

Write the letter of the term or phrase that best completes each sentence.

_____ 17. The AIDS virus attacks the body's _____ system.
    a. organ   **b.** immune   **c.** digestive   **d.** respiratory

_____ 18. Many drug users get the AIDS virus by _____ .
    a. hugging   **c.** using contaminated needles
    b. sharing drinking glasses   **d.** shaking hands

STUDY GUIDE

Chapter 8

Kingdom Monera

Text Pages 188–192

Write the letter of the term or phrase that best completes each sentence.

_____ 1. Organisms whose cells have no membrane-bound organelles are _____ .
   a. prokaryotes
   b. eukaryotes

_____ 2. Thousands of _____ live on and in your body.
   a. bacteria
   b. cyanobacteria

_____ 3. Organisms that use oxygen for respiration are _____ organisms.
   a. aerobic
   b. anaerobic

_____ 4. A _____ is a substance that absorbs light.
   a. bloom
   b. pigment

_____ 5. Some bacteria have a thick _____ that surrounds the cell wall.
   a. membrane
   b. capsule

_____ 6. Most bacteria reproduce by _____ .
   a. tubes
   b. fission

_____ 7. Monerans that live in your intestines are _____ bacteria.
   a. anaerobic
   b. aerobic

_____ 8. Some bacteria have a whiplike tail called a _____ .
   a. bloom
   b. flagellum

Under each picture, write the name of each kind of bacteria.

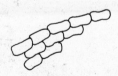

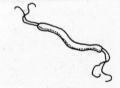

_____   _____   _____

STUDY GUIDE

Monerans in Your Life

*Cross out the statements that **DO NOT** agree with the textbook.*

1. Pasteurization is a process in which bacteria are killed by heating food to a high temperature.

2. Peanuts and peas have nitrogen-fixing bacteria in their roots.

3. Toxins are poisons produced by some bacteria.

4. All monerans are saprophytes.

5. Louis Pasteur was the first to produce endospores.

6. Bacteria cannot be killed by drugs of any kind.

7. An organism that uses dead material as a food and energy source is called a saprophyte.

8. Bacteria are helpful in producing cheese, butter, and yogurt.

9. Botulism bacteria save farmers millions of dollars a year.

10. Botulism endospores are heat resistant.

11. A disease-causing organism is called a pathogen.

12. Antibiotics kill bacteria.

13. Saprophytes have thick walls called endospores.

14. Pasteurization is only used to treat milk.

15. The thick-walled structures formed by some bacteria are called endospores.

Tell whether each of the following are harmful or helpful.

16. bacteria used to make foods: _____

17. pathogens: _____

18. saprophytes: _____

19. antibiotics: _____

20. toxins: _____

21. botulism bacteria: _____

22. nitrogen-fixing bacteria: _____

STUDY GUIDE   Chapter 9

Kingdom Protista   Text Pages 202–209

Write the letter of the term or phrase that best completes each sentence.

_____ 1. The cell walls of diatoms contain _____ .
   a. cilia   **b.** silica   **c.** chlorophyll   **d.** flagella

_____ 2. An amoeba is a kind of _____ .
   a. diatom   **b.** protozoan   **c.** algae   **d.** ciliate

_____ 3. A "red tide" is caused by an explosion of the one-celled _____ .
   a. paramecium   **b.** red algae   **c.** flagellates   **d.** dinoflagellates

_____ 4. All _____ have a nucleus.
   a. protists   **b.** monerans   **c.** prokaryotes   **d.** bacteria

_____ 5. Footlike extensions of cytoplasm are called _____ .
   a. pseudopods   **b.** cilia   **c.** flagella   **d.** algae

_____ 6. All _____ contain the pigment chlorophyll in their chloroplasts.
   a. protozoans   **b.** fungi   **c.** algae   **d.** bacteria

_____ 7. A kind of amoeba in the water can cause _____ .
   a. sleeping sickness **b.** worms   **c.** pseudopods   **d.** dysentery

_____ 8. Short, oarlike structures that extend from the cell membrane are _____ .
   a. flagella   **b.** protozoans   **c.** cilia   **d.** pseudopods

_____ 9. The animal-like protists are known as _____ .
   a. Chrysophyta   **b.** Protozoa   **c.** Euglenophyta   **d.** Pyrrophyta

_____ 10. The Irish potato famine of 1846-1847 was caused by a _____ .
   a. slime mold   **b.** protozoan   **c.** water mold   **d.** diatom

Use the pictures and information in your textbook to identify these protists. Write the correct name on the line beneath each picture.

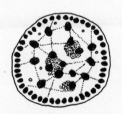 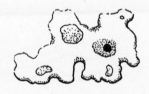 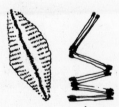

STUDY GUIDE

Chapter 9

Kingdom Fungi

Check (✓) the statements that agree with the textbook.

_____ 1. Yeasts can reproduce asexually by budding.

_____ 2. Fungi grow best in cool, dry areas.

_____ 3. *Penicillium* is an example of imperfect fungi.

_____ 4. Mushrooms are an example of a mutualistic relationship.

_____ 5. The body of a fungus usually consists of a mass of many-celled threadlike tubes called hyphae.

_____ 6. Fungi of Zygomycota produce spores in round spore cases called sporangia.

_____ 7. Club fungi produce spores in club-shaped structures called basidia.

_____ 8. Lichens consist of a fungus and cyanobacteria or green algae.

_____ 9. Fungi always feed on live organisms.

_____ 10. Chitin is a type of spore in club fungi.

_____ 11. Two organisms that benefit from living together are said to have a mutualistic relationship.

_____ 12. Certain species of imperfect fungi cause ringworm and athlete's foot.

_____ 13. Lichens are the fungi used on pizzas.

_____ 14. Saprophytes obtain food by feeding on dead organisms.

_____ 15. The black fuzz on old bread is a type of zygote fungus.

Study the illustration below and answer the following questions.

16. To what kingdom do these organisms belong? _____

17. To what division do these organisms belong? _____

18. What structures do these organisms use for reproduction? _____

19. What is the common name of these organisms? _____

20. Where do these organisms grow best? _____

Fungus—Can't Live Without It

*Cross out the statements that **DO NOT** agree with the textbook.*

1. Viruses do not have enzymes or organelles.

2. Antibiotics will kill anything.

3. Penicillin is produced by the fungus *Penicillium chrysogenum*.

4. Antibiotics prevent some diseases by preventing bacteria from reproducing and growing.

5. Encephalitis is carried by rats.

6. No drugs are available that treat infections caused by viruses.

7. Antibiotic drugs were introduced in the 1940s.

8. Encephalitis is an inflammation of the brain, spinal cord, and nerves leading from the spinal cord.

9. Streptomycin, tetracycline, and erythromycin are antibiotics.

10. Developing antiviral drugs is relatively cheap to do.

11. Some people cannot be treated by antibiotics because of allergic reactions.

12. The first antiviral drug was made in the 1920s.

13. The first antiviral drug was produced from a species of fungi.

14. Most bacterial infections can be cured with antibiotics.

15. Antibiotics are chemicals that have a harmful effect on bacteria.

STUDY GUIDE

Characteristics of Plants

Part A

Use the clues to fill in the boxes and to complete the word puzzle. Then answer the riddle below.

What goes around a room and around plant cells? _____

1. ☐ __ __ __ __

2. __ ☐ __ __ __ __ __ __ __ __ __ __ __

3. __ ☐ __ __ __

4. __ __ __ __ __ ☐ __

5. __ __ __ __ __ __ ☐ __ __ __ __ __

Clues

1. needed by all plants to carry nutrients to cells and wastes away from cells
2. red, yellow, or orange pigments found within chloroplasts
3. a many-celled organism that can make its own food and that usually contains chlorophyll
4. waxy, protective layer coating some stems and leaves
5. Bryophytes are often referred to as _____ plants.

Part B

Answer the following questions.

1. What is the organic compound that makes cell walls rigid? _____

2. The oldest plant fossils are from the Devonian period. How old are those fossils?

   _____

3. What is the name of the plant division that includes the mosses and liverworts?

   _____

4. What is the pigment found in most plant cells? _____

5. What type of plant has tubes that transport materials from place to place within the plant?

   _____

STUDY GUIDE   Chapter 10

Seedless Plants   Text Pages 236–245

In the blank, write the term that best matches each phrase.

moss   rhizoids
liverwort   sporophyte
protonema   pioneer species
alternation of generations   fern
vascular tissue   rhizome
epiphyte   sori
frond   gametophyte

_____ **1.** the form of a moss plant that produces gametes

_____ **2.** a simple, rootless plant with leaflike growths that form a spiral around a structure that resembles a stem

_____ **3.** a continual cycle that alternates between the sporophyte and game-tophyte

_____ **4.** structures that produce spores and are found on the lower surface of a fern leaf

_____ **5.** rootlike filament of a moss

_____ **6.** the form of the moss plant that produces spores

_____ **7.** a simple, rootless plant that has a flattened, leaflike body

_____ **8.** the first plants to grow in a new or disturbed area

_____ **9.** the underground stem of a fern

_____ **10.** long, tubular cells that carry water, minerals, and nutrients through some types of plants

_____ **11.** the leaf of a fern

_____ **12.** a plant that grows on another plant for support

_____ **13.** a threadlike green structure that results from a germinating moss spore

_____ **14.** the largest group of seedless vascular plants

STUDY GUIDE

Peat Moss as Fuel

Answer the following questions.

1. What are bogs? _____

_____

2. What is peat? _____

_____

_____

3. How is coal formed? _____

_____

4. Why might peat be a good source of fuel for New England? _____

_____

_____

_____

5. What are two consequences to the environment if peat is burned as fuel? _____

_____

_____

6. How would using peat as fuel in the United States affect the bogs? _____

_____

_____

_____

STUDY GUIDE   Chapter 11

Seed Plants   Text Pages 254–258

Check (✔) the statements that agree with the textbook.

_____ 1. Most scientists classify seed plants into two major groups, the gymnosperms and angio-sperms.

_____ 2. Monocots are flowering plants with flower parts in fours or fives.

_____ 3. The conifers include oaks and maples.

_____ 4. Gymnosperms are vascular plants that produce seeds on the scales of cones.

_____ 5. Angiosperms take in huge amounts of carbon dioxide for photosynthesis and release oxygen needed by other organisms.

_____ 6. A cotyledon is a seed leaf inside a seed.

_____ 7. Seed plants have no roots or stems.

_____ 8. Angiosperms form the basis for the diets of most animals, including humans.

_____ 9. Ginkgos are a modern form of angiosperm.

_____ 10. In dicots, the vascular bundles show up as branching, netlike veins in the broad dicot leaves.

_____ 11. In monocots, the vascular bundles show up as parallel veins in the narrow leaves.

_____ 12. Gymnosperms are not economically important plants.

_____ 13. Flowering plants have existed since the beginning of time.

_____ 14. Pines, spruces, cedars, and junipers all belong to the division Coniferophyta.

_____ 15. A fruit is a ripened ovary, the part of the plant where seeds are formed.

_____ 16. Gymnosperms are the most common form of plant life on Earth today.

_____ 17. Most gymnosperms are evergreen plants that keep their leaves for several years.

_____ 18. Within a seed plant are all the parts needed to produce a new plant.

_____ 19. Gymnosperms produce only white flowers.

_____ 20. Angiosperms are used in the production of medicines, perfumes, and pesticides.

STUDY GUIDE   Chapter 11

Parts of Complex Plants   Text Pages 259–261

Write the letter of the term or phrase that best completes each statement.

_____ **1.** Carrots and beets are _____ .
    a. roots that carry on photosynthesis
    b. roots swollen with stored food

_____ **2.** Xylem and phloem tissues are located in the _____ of a leaf.
    a. spongy layer   **b.** stomata

_____ **3.** Sugar cane has an aboveground stem that stores large quantities of _____ .
    a. minerals   **b.** food

_____ **4.** The small pores in a leaf surface are called _____ .
    a. guard cells   **b.** stomata

_____ **5.** Tubular cells that move food from leaves and stems to other parts of the plant are called _____ .
    a. cambium   **b.** phloem

_____ **6.** The cells of a leaf's _____ are packed with chloroplasts filled with chlorophyll.
    a. epidermis   **b.** palisade layer

_____ **7.** Roots move water and _____ from the soil through the stems to the leaves.
    a. minerals   **b.** food

_____ **8.** The thin layer of cells that covers the upper and lower surfaces of a leaf is called the _____ .
    a. epidermis   **b.** spongy layer

_____ **9.** The _____ open and close the stomata.
    a. phloem   **b.** guard cells

_____ **10.** The trunk of a tree is actually a _____ .
    a. root   **b.** stem

_____ **11.** Oak, birch, and other trees have _____ stems.
    a. woody   **b.** herbaceous

Label the diagram below using the following terms: xylem, phloem, and cambium.

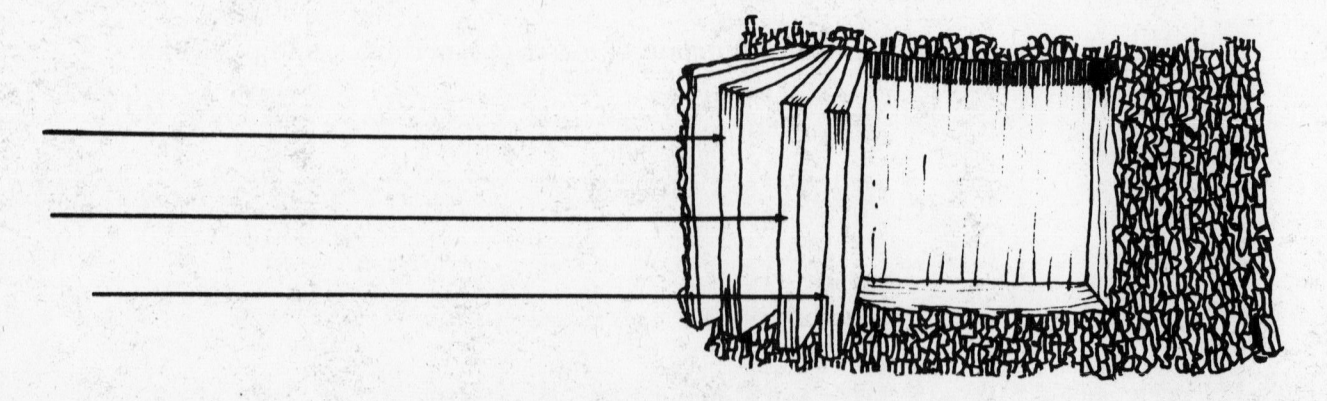

STUDY GUIDE

Seed Plant Reproduction

Check (✔) the statements that agree with the textbook.

_____ 1. Pollination is the transfer of pollen grains from the stamen to ovules.

_____ 2. A seed always germinates within a month after reaching the soil.

_____ 3. On a pine tree's female cones, two ovules are produced on top of each scale.

_____ 4. The stamen is the male reproductive organ of a flower.

_____ 5. Flowers with a lot of color are usually pollinated by the wind.

_____ 6. A flower is pollinated when pollen grains land on the sticky stamen.

_____ 7. Sepals are small, leaflike parts of a flower that cover the bud.

_____ 8. Flowers are the reproductive organs of gymnosperms.

_____ 9. In pine trees, pollen grains develop in the male cones.

_____ 10. Seeds often remain dormant until conditions are right for germination.

_____ 11. The pistil is the female reproductive organ of the flower.

_____ 12. Dry fruits include pears, tomatoes, and peaches.

_____ 13. Almost all pollen grains reach the female cones.

_____ 14. The ovary is the swollen base of the pistil where ovules are formed.

_____ 15. In pine trees, a pollen tube grows from the pollen grain to the ovule.

Match the lettered structure on the diagram with the correct term on the left.

_____ 1. pistil

_____ 2. stamen

_____ 3. petal

_____ 4. sepal

_____ 5. ovary

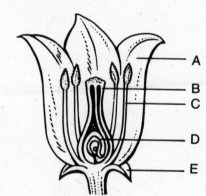

STUDY GUIDE

Effects of Acid Rain

*Cross out the statements that **DO NOT** agree with the textbook.*

1. European countries have no acid rain problems.

2. All of the acid rain in Canada results from pollution produced in Canada.

3. A scrubber blows a fine mist of water through the gases released from burning fuel.

4. Acid rain contains sulfur dioxide and nitrogen oxide that were released into the air as pollution.

5. Acid rain causes the chemistry of soil to change.

6. Acid rain does not include snow or fog.

7. Only a few lakes in Canada and the United States have been affected by acid rain.

8. About 75 percent of the acid rain in some parts of Canada is the result of pollution from the United States.

9. Outdoor artwork can be harmed by acid rain.

10. Acid rain is sometimes a thousand times more acidic than normal rain.

11. Scrubbers are cheap to use and install.

12. Nitrogen oxides are released by automobile exhausts.

13. Many forests in Europe have been badly damaged by acid rain.

14. The maple syrup industry in the United States and Canada has been harmed by acid rain.

15. Studies show that decreasing the amount of chemicals released into the air decreases the harm done to Earth.

16. Acid rain can be in the form of rain, snow, or fog.

17. Buildings are too solid to be affected by acid rain.

18. Fish cannot be harmed by acid rain.

19. A source of sulfur dioxide pollution is power generating stations that burn coal.

20. Sulfur dioxide and nitrogen oxide combine with water vapor in the air to form hydrochloric acid and nitric acid.

NAME _____ DATE _____ CLASS _____

Photosynthesis and Respiration
Text Pages 276–281

Write the correct term from the textbook next to each description.

_____ 1. control size of stoma opening

_____ 2. enters through stomata

_____ 3. released through stomata

_____ 4. loss of water vapor

_____ 5. masked by green pigments in the spring and summer

_____ 6. traps light energy during photosynthesis

_____ 7. sugar formed during photosynthesis

_____ 8. gaseous product of photosynthesis

_____ 9. process that releases energy

_____ 10. process that stores energy

Complete the following sentences using appropriate words from the textbook.

11. Leaves have more _____ on the lower surface.

12. More water is lost through _____ than is used during photosynthesis.

13. Water is lost in the form of _____ .

14. Photosynthesis is a process in which energy is _____ .

15. $C_6H_{12}O_6$ is the chemical formula for _____ .

16. Photosynthesis occurs only in cells containing _____ .

17. Water is split by energy from _____ .

18. During photosynthesis, plants remove _____ from the air.

19. _____ occurs in all cells of all organisms.

a stoma

STUDY GUIDE

Plant Responses

Write the letter of the correct term next to each description.

_____ **1.** affects behavior of an organism

_____ **2.** response of a plant to a stimulus

_____ **3.** grow away from

_____ **4.** grow toward

_____ **5.** response of plants to light

_____ **6.** response of plants to gravity

_____ **7.** flowering response to changes in the lengths of light and dark in a day

_____ **8.** control plant tropisms

_____ **9.** causes fruit to ripen

a. negative tropism

b. plant hormones

c. gravitropism

d. ethylene gas

e. photoperiodism

f. phototropism

g. stimulus

h. tropism

i. positive tropism

Place a check (✓) next to the sentences that agree with the textbook. Rewrite the other sentences so that they agree.

_____ **10.** Plant roots tend to grow upward in response to gravity.

_____ **11.** Plants that bend toward light are exhibiting positive photoperiodism.

_____ **12.** If you plant a seed upside down, the stem will still grow upward.

_____ **13.** Most plants need a certain period of darkness to promote flowering.

_____ **14.** Auxins control phototropism in plants.

_____ **15.** Ethylene gas causes plants to grow taller.

_____ **16.** Day-neutral plants will flower over a wide range of dark periods.

_____ **17.** Long-day plants need short nights to flower.

STUDY GUIDE

Plant Relationships

Place a check (✓) next to the sentences that agree with the textbook. Rewrite the other sentences so that they agree.

_____ **1.** Parasitism can occur between members of the same species.

_____ **2.** Bats are important pollinators.

_____ **3.** Parasitic plants are sometimes mistaken for fungi.

_____ **4.** In a mutualistic relationship, both parties benefit.

_____ **5.** On islands where there are no tortoises, opuntia cacti grow taller.

_____ **6.** Coevolution occurs over a long period of time.

Use the following clues to complete the puzzle.

Across

4. Mutualistic relationships between plants and insects often involve _____ .

6. A successful parasite does not usually kill its _____ .

7. Thorny acacia trees of Central America and Africa often house _____ .

8. A relationship between two species that benefits both is _____ .

Down

1. Charles Darwin observed how tortoises and _____ cacti had evolved on the Galapagos Islands.

2. _____ occurs when two or more species evolve together.

3. The Indian Pipe has no _____ in its leaves.

5. A _____ lives on or in another organism, getting nutrients from that organism.

NAME _____ DATE _____ CLASS _____

The Treasure of Tropical Plants

Complete the following sentences using words from the following list.

drugs	National Cancer Institute	word-of-mouth	deforestation
document	tumors	healers	ethnobotany

1. The study of people and their use of plants is called _____ .

2. Cultures that have traditional healers rely on _____ to hand down their knowledge of medicinal plants.

3. Funding for collecting and testing tropical plants has come from the

   _____ .

4. Many _____ we use today are derived from common plants.

5. Traditional _____ know how local plants can be used for medical treatment.

6. More and more species of plants are being lost because of tropical _____ .

7. Researchers must carefully _____ the knowledge of traditional healers.

8. Scientists are testing tropical plants for their ability to slow or stop the growth of

   _____ .

Place a check (✓) next to the following sentences that agree with the textbook. Rewrite the other sentences so that they agree.

_____ 9. Deforestation is mainly a problem that affects humans.

_____ 10. Many of the drugs and medications we use today are derived from common plants.

_____ 11. Traditional healers have kept careful written records for thousands of years.

_____ 12. Thousands of hectares of tropical forests are cut or burned every day.

_____ 13. The National Cancer Institute is funding investigations to stop deforestation.

_____ 14. Ethnobotanists have only investigated a few of the remaining tribes in the tropics.

_____ 15. Rosy periwinkle grows on the island of Madagascar.

_____ 16. Acacia trees contain chemicals used to treat leukemia and Hodgkin's disease.

STUDY GUIDE

Chapter 13

What Is an Animal?

Text Pages 302–304

Check (✔) the statements that agree with the textbook.

_____ 1. Animal cells are eukaryotic.

_____ 2. Animals digest their food. The food must be broken down in molecules small enough for their bodies to use.

_____ 3. Most animals are unicellular.

_____ 4. Without sunlight, animals cannot digest their food.

_____ 5. Animals move from place to place.

_____ 6. Animal cells are prokaryotic.

_____ 7. Animals have many cells, and different cells carry out different functions.

_____ 8. Animals can't use the proteins, fats, and carbohydrates in foods directly.

_____ 9. Animals do not depend on other living things for food.

_____ 10. Animals that move very slowly have adaptations that let them take care of their needs.

_____ 11. Animal cells have a nucleus and organelles surrounded by membranes.

Label the following animals with the kind of symmetry each has.

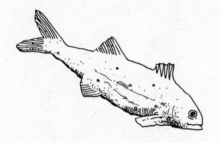 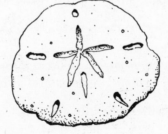 

12. _____   13. _____   14. _____

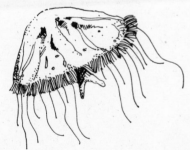 

15. _____   16. _____   17. _____

STUDY GUIDE

Experiments Using Animals

*Cross out the statements that **DO NOT** agree with the textbook.*

1. Many people believe all animals have rights.

2. In the United States, there is only one large animal rights group.

3. Experiments on animals help test drugs that fight human diseases.

4. All drugs are tried on humans before they are tried on animals.

5. Cats are used to learn about the dangerous effects of drug addiction.

6. Malaria has killed more people in the world than any other disease.

7. Each year, about 100 million animals are used for research, education, or product testing.

8. Enzymes taken from pig stomachs are used to help people with cystic fibrosis digest food.

9. All animal rights groups feel that dissections of animals are necessary.

10. All scientists hate animals, especially the ones in labs.

11. Animals in experiments often experience pain and distress.

12. Experiments on animals have helped in the development of vaccines.

13. Experiments on animals help in fighting many diseases, with the exception of cancer.

14. Surgeons first practice organ transplants on cows and other animals.

15. Many animal rights groups are opposed to the conditions in which lab animals are being kept.

*Who would more likely say each of the following statements, an animal rights activist or a scientific researcher who experiments on animals? Write either **A** for animal rights activist or **R** for researcher.*

_____ 16. "A human life is worth the sacrifice of some animals."

_____ 17. "Animal experiments are important for testing new surgical techniques."

_____ 18. "All life forms should be treated with respect."

_____ 19. "You may be alive today because of experiments on animals."

_____ 20. "Many animals suffer terribly in scientific labs."

_____ 21. "Dissections of animals are unnecessary."

STUDY GUIDE

Chapter 13

The Simplest Invertebrates

Text Pages 308–313

Write the letter of the term or phrase that best completes each statement.

_____ 1. A sponge is covered with many small openings called _____ .
   a. larva   b. pores   c. polyps   d. filters

_____ 2. The ability of an organism to replace body parts is called _____ .
   a. regeneration   b. reproduction   c. restitution   d. reintroduction

_____ 3. All cnidarians have _____ .
   a. reverse symmetry b. radial symmetry c. bilateral symmetry d. radical symmetry

_____ 4. Cells that line the inside of a sponge are called _____ .
   a. collar cells   b. polyps   c. filter feeders   d. medusa

_____ 5. Organisms that are attached to one place throughout their life span are _____ .
   a. cnidarians   b. filter feeders   c. sessile   d. medusa

_____ 6. The phylum name of sponges is _____ .
   a. Precambrium   b. Cnidarian   c. Porifera   d. Spongerium

Use the diagram to answer the following questions.

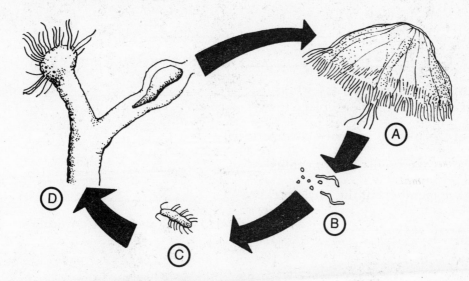

7. This diagram illustrates reproduction of what form of cnidarians? _____

8. What does the free-swimming medusa release into the water? _____

9. Is that release part of sexual reproduction or asexual reproduction? _____

10. What do the fertilized eggs grow into? _____ Which drawing represents that? _____

11. In the next step, has the cnidarian become a medusa or a polyp? _____

12. What buds off a polyp to complete the cycle? _____

13. Is the budding a form of sexual or asexual reproduction? _____

STUDY GUIDE

The Simple Worms

Complete the following sentences using the appropriate terms from the textbook.

1. The worms called _____ use hooks and suckers to attach themselves to the intestine of a host organism.

2. The roundworms have a digestive system with a(n) _____ and an anus.

3. You can get sick by eating undercooked _____ that contains _____ cysts.

4. Worms with flattened bodies are called _____ .

5. Worms have _____ symmetry.

6. Humans can get _____ by walking barefoot over soil.

7. An example of a free-living class of flatworms are the _____ .

8. Masses of _____ worms can block the intestines of animals and cause death.

9. A tapeworm can grow to be _____ long.

10. Dogs can get _____ through a mosquito bite.

11. Parasites live off other organisms, while _____ organisms don't depend on others for food or a place to live.

12. The body of a planarian is usually covered with _____ .

13. Roundworms make up the phylum called _____ .

14. Flatworms are members of the phylum called _____ .

15. A _____ is a young worm with a protective covering.

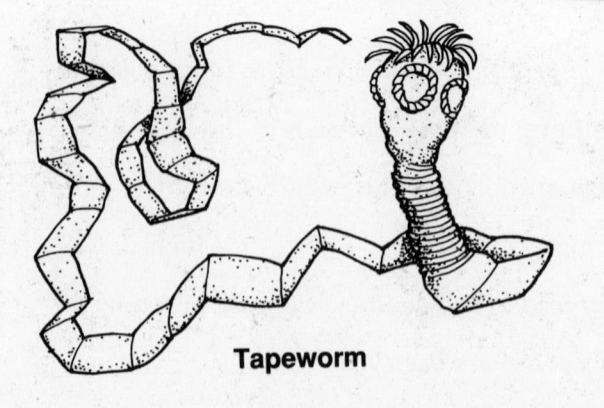

Tapeworm

STUDY GUIDE

Chapter 14

Mollusks

Text Pages 324–326

*Cross out the statements that **DO NOT** agree with the textbook.*

1. Bivalves have a shell divided into two parts joined by a hinge.

2. Mollusks come in only one shape.

3. Cephalopods include snails, slugs, abalones, and conches.

4. The mantle of a mollusk is a covering over the soft body.

5. Bivalves are very well adapted to living in water.

6. The gills of a mollusk are in the mantle cavity.

7. Cephalopods create pearls with their tentacles.

8. The empty shells of mollusks provide homes for hermit crabs.

9. Univalves move by muscular contractions of the foot.

10. The word *mollusk* comes from a Latin word meaning "two shelled."

11. Clams, oysters, and scallops are all univalves.

12. The radula is a tongue-like organ of univalves that works like a file with rows of teeth.

13. No univalve is able to live on land.

14. Most mollusks have an open circulatory system.

15. Unlike the other mollusks, cephalopods have a closed circulatory system.

Identify the following as a univalve, bivalve, or cephalopod.

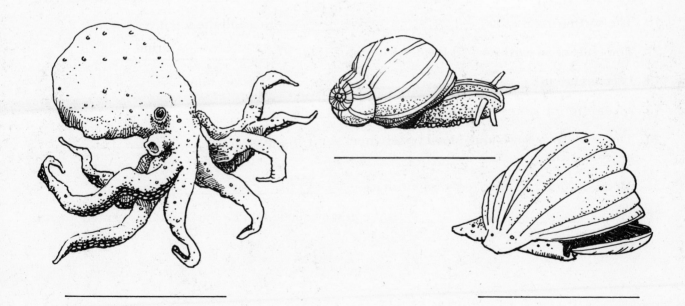

_____   _____

STUDY GUIDE

Segmented Worms

Check (✓) the statements that agree with the textbook.

_____ 1. The lungs of worms are directly related to the gills of mollusks.

_____ 2. Setae are the bristle-like structures on the outside of an earthworm's body.

_____ 3. Worms and leeches are in the phylum Annelida.

_____ 4. Five pairs of aortic arches pump blood through an earthworm's body.

_____ 5. Leeches only feed on the blood of humans.

_____ 6. The earthworm nerve cord connects the crop to the intestine.

_____ 7. The gizzard is a muscular structure that grinds soil.

_____ 8. Earthworms have an open circulatory system.

_____ 9. The crop of an earthworm is a sac used for storage.

_____ 10. Mollusks and segmented worms probably share a common ancestor.

_____ 11. Earthworms have two blood vessels that run along the sides of the body.

_____ 12. The earthworm intestine is called a setae.

_____ 13. Leeches secrete a substance to keep blood from clotting.

_____ 14. Every segment of an earthworm is different from all the other segments.

_____ 15. The first stage of development in both the mollusks and the segmented worms is a structure called a larva.

Complete the following sentences using appropriate words from the textbook.

16. The earthworm uses its _____ to grind the soil it eats.

17. The body of an earthworm is divided into more than 100 _____ .

18. Leeches use two _____ to attach to an animal.

19. An earthworm stores soil in its _____ .

20. The earthworm's two long blood vessels meet at the organism's _____ , or front, end.

21. An earthworm can cling to the soil with its _____ .

22. The _____ is the best evidence that mollusks and segmented worms share a common ancestor.

STUDY GUIDE

Arthropods

Write the letter of the term that best completes each sentence.

_____ 1. The largest group of complex invertebrates are the _____ .
    a. millipedes   **b.** insects

_____ 2. The series of changes many insects go through to become adults is called _____ .
    a. dividing   **b.** metamorphosis

_____ 3. The largest phylum of animals is the phylum _____ .
    a. Arthropoda   **b.** Insecta

_____ 4. Maggots and caterpillars are examples of _____ .
    a. larvae   **b.** arachnids

_____ 5. Spiders and ticks are examples of _____ .
    a. insects   **b.** arachnids

_____ 6. From time to time, an arthropod will shed its _____ .
    a. thorax   **b.** exoskeleton

_____ 7. Lobsters and shrimp are examples of _____ .
    a. crustaceans   **b.** chitin

_____ 8. Structures that grow from the body are called _____ .
    a. mandibles   **b.** appendages

_____ 9. The openings in a spider's abdomen that allow movement of oxygen and carbon dioxide into and out of the book lungs are called _____ .
    a. spiracles   **b.** swimmerets

_____ 10. Animals that look like worms but have legs include centipedes and _____ .
    a. insects   **b.** millipedes

_____ 11. Insects have _____ body regions.
    a. three   **b.** two

_____ 12. The process of replacing an exoskeleton is called _____ .
    a. molting   **b.** metamorphosis

_____ 13. The jaws of crustaceans are called _____ .
    a. appendages   **b.** mandibles

_____ 14. The arthropods with eight legs are the _____ .
    a. insects   **b.** arachnids

STUDY GUIDE

Pesticides

*Cross out the statements that **DO NOT** agree with the textbook.*

1. Pesticides decrease the amount of crops harvested.

2. Many insects are harmless.

3. About 45 000 human poisonings due to pesticides are reported every year.

4. Pesticides cause about $1 billion worth of damage to the environment each year.

5. Humans are not affected by pesticide vapors.

6. The praying mantis eats harmful insects.

7. Few species of plants and animals are affected by pesticides.

8. DDT is in wide use in the United States.

9. Pesticides often either miss the target plant or drip off the plant into the soil.

10. About 99 percent of a pesticide goes into the soil, water, or air.

11. Farmers lose money on pesticides.

12. Large amounts of pesticides enter aquatic environments because of runoff from farm fields.

13. Pesticides are chemicals that kill undesirable plants and insects.

14. Human water supplies never become contaminated with pesticides.

15. Often less than .01 percent of a pesticide actually reaches its target.

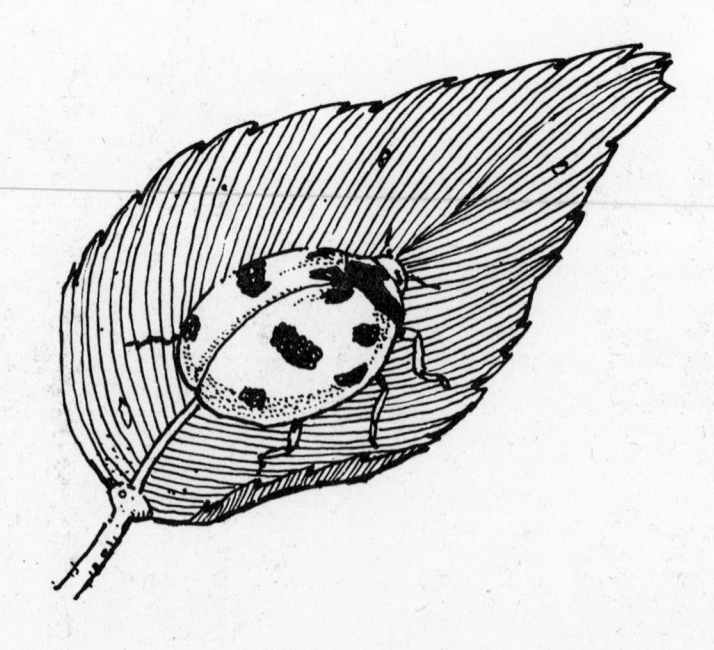

NAME _____ DATE _____ CLASS _____

STUDY GUIDE

Chapter 14

Echinoderms

Text Pages 342–344

Check (✔) the statements that agree with the textbook.

_____ 1. The echinoderms are the most primitive form of invertebrates.

_____ 2. Sea stars feed on mollusks by using the suction power of their tube feet.

_____ 3. Echinoderms live on the ocean bottom.

_____ 4. A characteristic of echinoderms is radial symmetry.

_____ 5. The name *echinoderm* means "scaly-skin."

_____ 6. Oyster farmers love to see echinoderms in their oyster beds.

_____ 7. The water vascular system is a network of water-filled canals.

_____ 8. Spines cover the outside of echinoderms.

_____ 9. The bodies of echinoderms are divided into seven sections located around a central point.

_____ 10. The tube feet of echinoderms are connected to the water vascular system.

_____ 11. Sand dollars are not echinoderms but a form of mollusk.

_____ 12. A sea star uses its spines to attack clams.

_____ 13. A sea star can regrow lost arms.

_____ 14. To eat a clam, a sea star turns its stomach inside out.

Match the echinoderm with the illustrations by writing the correct letter next to the organism's name.

_____ 15. sea star

_____ 16. sea urchin

_____ 17. sand dollar

_____ 18. brittle star

_____ 19. sea cucumber

a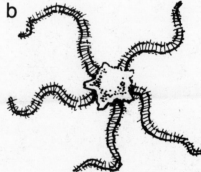
b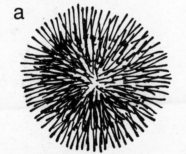
c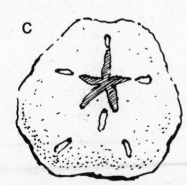
d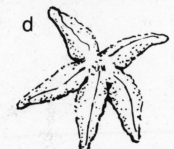
e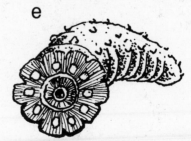

STUDY GUIDE

Fish

Write the letter of the term or phrase that best completes each sentence.

_____ 1. The internal skeleton of a chordate is the _____.
   a. notochord   b. cartilage   c. gill slit   d. endoskeleton

_____ 2. A _____ is an organism that kills other organisms for food.
   a. tunicate   b. predator   c. chordate   d. lancelet

_____ 3. The bundle of nerves that lies above the notochord is the _____.
   a. gill slit   b. dorsal nerve cord   c. cartilage   d. endoskeleton

_____ 4. The thin, hard plates that cover a fish's body are _____.
   a. scales   b. chordates   c. tunicates   d. fins

_____ 5. All fish are _____ animals.
   a. warm-blooded   b. cartilaginous   c. cold-blooded   d. bony

_____ 6. The flexible, rodlike structure along the back of a chordate is the _____.
   a. fin   b. dorsal nerve cord   c. notochord   d. lancelet

_____ 7. Structures in a fish's throat area that take in oxygen are _____.
   a. gills   b. fins   c. scales   d. notochords

_____ 8. A tough, flexible tissue that is not as hard as bone is _____.
   a. endoskeleton   b. tunicate   c. scale   d. cartilage

_____ 9. An organism that is killed and eaten by a shark is the shark's _____.
   a. predator   b. tunicate   c. prey   d. chordate

_____ 10. The fanlike structures used for steering are the _____.
   a. scales   b. fins   c. gills   d. swim bladders

Write the common class name of each fish shown.

11. _____

shark

12. _____

lamprey

13. _____

salmon

STUDY GUIDE
Chapter 15

Amphibians
Text Pages 356–359

Check (✔) the statements that agree with the textbook.

_____ 1. Scientists think that lobe-finned fish evolved from amphibians.

_____ 2. An amphibian's period of inactivity in the hot summer is called estivation.

_____ 3. Toads return to the water to lay their eggs.

_____ 4. Salamanders are a cross between a fish and a lizard.

_____ 5. Amphibians are cold-blooded vertebrates.

_____ 6. The first stage of a frog's metamorphosis is the larva stage.

_____ 7. The bulging eyes and nostrils on top of a frog's head help it see and breathe while almost totally submerged in water.

_____ 8. Less food and cooler temperatures quicken a frog's metamorphosis.

_____ 9. Salamanders hunt during the day and rest at night to avoid the coldness after the sun goes down.

_____ 10. The period of inactivity in the winter is called hibernation.

_____ 11. A frog's tongue is attached to the front of its mouth.

_____ 12. Frogs have no lungs.

_____ 13. Bullfrogs may not go through metamorphosis for over a year after hatching.

_____ 14. Amphibians faced fierce competition on land when they evolved 350 million years ago.

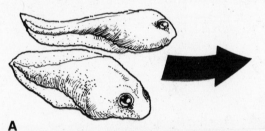

A   B

15. What process is shown above? _____

_____

16. Figure A represents what stage? _____

17. Figure B represents what stage? _____

STUDY GUIDE

Chapter 15

Amphibian Population Decline

Text Pages 360–361

*Cross out the statements that **DO NOT** agree with the textbook.*

1. Destruction of native habitats contributes to amphibian population decline.

2. Species of amphibians all over the world have been declining over the last 20 years.

3. Acid rain is especially harmful to frogs because of their permeable skin.

4. When a forest has been clear-cut, acid rain increases.

5. Species that reflect the condition of the environment are known as biological indicators.

6. Amphibians require dry habitats to breed.

7. Pesticides do not hurt amphibians because pesticides only harm insects.

8. Huge populations of certain frog species have grown in recent years.

9. We contribute to acid rain by driving in cars and flying on airplanes.

10. When a forest is clear-cut, all the trees are completely removed.

11. Scientists think that the rapid loss of amphibians is a reflection of the deterioration of our environment.

12. Urban areas are decreasing and wetlands are increasing in the United States.

13. Eliminating wetlands eliminates breeding grounds for amphibians.

14. When an area is clear-cut, frogs seem to increase in population.

15. Humans may contribute to declining amphibian populations by eating frog legs in restaurants.

Unscramble the following terms and then find them in the puzzle below.

tidoracni   mpihaainb   dcia nari

relac-utc   outillpno   ogrfs

```
C R G N A I B I H P M A R E W U T
A A B D T U S F X C W V P D B R D
Z I B E C A P L A Y N M O U I O Q
S G O R F T C S N E C L B A T R
F Z X C V A T I G K P I L V B A C
T O H S I Y V Q D H R C U I O C U
P J D Q Y D O O F R T U T E H I L
J F I B F S D U L Z A B I X J D K
O I U U Y T R E W C R I O M O N W
P C L E A R C U T D F B N L P I K
J O I N B H U Y G V C F T K R S O
```

STUDY GUIDE

Reptiles

Check (✔) the statements that agree with the textbook.

_____ **1.** A reptile's heart has three chambers.

_____ **2.** Amphibians evolved from the early reptiles.

_____ **3.** Reptiles live on every continent of the world.

_____ **4.** An amniotic egg provides a complete environment in which an embryo can develop.

_____ **5.** A reptile is a cold-blooded vertebrate.

_____ **6.** Reptiles need a moist environment in which to lay their eggs.

_____ **7.** Reptiles have gills rather than lungs.

_____ **8.** After an egg is fertilized, a female reptile secretes a leathery shell around the egg.

_____ **9.** The food supply for a growing embryo is the yolk.

_____ **10.** A reptile's claws prevent it from climbing or running.

_____ **11.** The pores in the shell of a reptile's egg stop the harmful flow of gases.

_____ **12.** There were at least two species of ancient flying reptiles.

_____ **13.** Reptiles' eggs are fertilized internally.

_____ **14.** Reptiles only have one basic shape.

_____ **15.** No reptiles live in Antarctica.

_____ **16.** The membranes in an amniotic egg protect the embryo.

Circle the two reptiles that are in the same order.

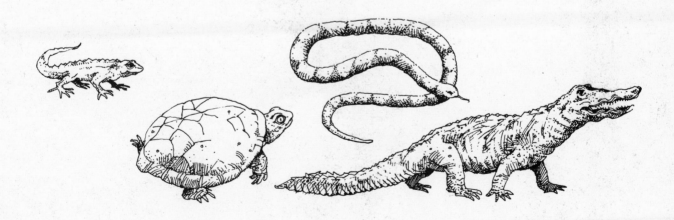

STUDY GUIDE

Chapter 16

Birds

Text Pages 372–377

Check (✔) the statements that agree with the textbook.

_____ 1. Down feathers provide an insulating layer next to the skin of adult birds.

_____ 2. Penguins use wings to swim under water.

_____ 3. Each lung of a bird has four different chambers.

_____ 4. The earliest bird fossil belongs to the genus *Archaeopteryx*.

_____ 5. Flight requires keen vision but poor hearing so that birds are not bothered by loud noises while they watch for prey.

_____ 6. All birds are warm-blooded animals.

_____ 7. Birds use their contour feathers to fly.

_____ 8. Food passes from a bird's mouth into its crop, where it is moistened and stored.

_____ 9. Bird fossils are some of the most common found by scientists.

_____ 10. The flightless birds cannot fly because they have no wings.

_____ 11. Most of a bird's bones are hollow.

_____ 12. Bird eggs are usually incubated by a parent until they hatch.

_____ 13. Preening is the process of rubbing oil over the feathers.

_____ 14. The hearts of some birds can beat almost 2000 times a minute.

_____ 15. Some birds can digest food in less than an hour.

STUDY GUIDE

Mammals

Write the letter of the term or phrase that best completes each statement.

_____ 1. Animals that eat plants are called _____ .
  a. herbivores **b.** mammals **c.** carnivores **d.** omnivores

_____ 2. A kangaroo is an example of a _____ .
  a. monotreme **b.** placenta **c.** marsupial **d.** primate

_____ 3. The milk that female mammals feed to their young is produced in the _____ glands.
  a. scent **b.** placental **c.** mammary **d.** oil

_____ 4. The _____ attaches the placenta to the embryo.
  a. umbilical cord **b.** mammary gland **c.** omnivore **d.** monotreme

_____ 5. The specialized teeth that bite and cut are the _____ .
  a. molars **b.** incisors **c.** canine teeth **d.** premolars

_____ 6. Whales and dolphins are examples of _____ .
  a. primates **b.** cetaceans **c.** fish **d.** perissodactyls

_____ 7. Animals that eat both plants and animals are called _____ .
  a. carnivores **b.** monotremes **c.** omnivores **d.** herbivores

_____ 8. The time during which the embryo develops in the mammal uterus is called the _____ .
  a. lagomorph **b.** gestation period **c.** marsupial **d.** umbilical cord

_____ 9. Mammals that lay eggs are known as _____ .
  a. marsupials **b.** carnivores **c.** monotremes **d.** placenta

_____ 10. After birth, a kangaroo spends a few months in a _____ .
  a. pouch **b.** placenta **c.** mammary gland **d.** monotreme

_____ 11. Animals that eat meat are called _____ .
  a. herbivores **b.** carnivores **c.** monotremes **d.** omnivores

_____ 12. Mammals have a _____ -chambered heart.
  a. two **b.** four **c.** six **d.** eight

_____ 13. Mammals are warm-blooded animals that have _____ on their bodies.
  a. feathers **b.** scales **c.** hair **d.** shells

Tasmanian devil, a marsupial

STUDY GUIDE

Saving the Manatee

*Cross out the statements that **DO NOT** agree with the textbook.*

1. Illegal hunting of manatees is called poaching.

2. Many manatees are killed by herbicides used to kill aquatic plants.

3. Manatees are carnivores that eat shrimp and other small animals.

4. Development in Florida has meant a loss of habitat for manatees.

5. Manatees love to swim in cold waters.

6. Manatees are too quick for hunters who are not experienced.

7. One characteristic of manatees is a high rate of population growth.

8. Manatees belong to the order Sirenia.

9. Barges and motorboats often collide with manatees.

10. Creating more refuges that do not allow motorboats might help save the manatees.

11. Manatees can only live in the open ocean.

12. A nickname for manatees is "sea cows."

13. Manatees have not yet been protected by law.

14. One way to save manatees would be to allow high speeds only on the Intracoastal Waterway.

15. An adult manatee weighs about half a ton.

16. Extinction may not be far away for the manatee.

17. By 1989, about 12 million manatees could be found in U.S. waters.

18. Manatees live in the rivers, estuaries, and coasts in tropical and subtropical regions.

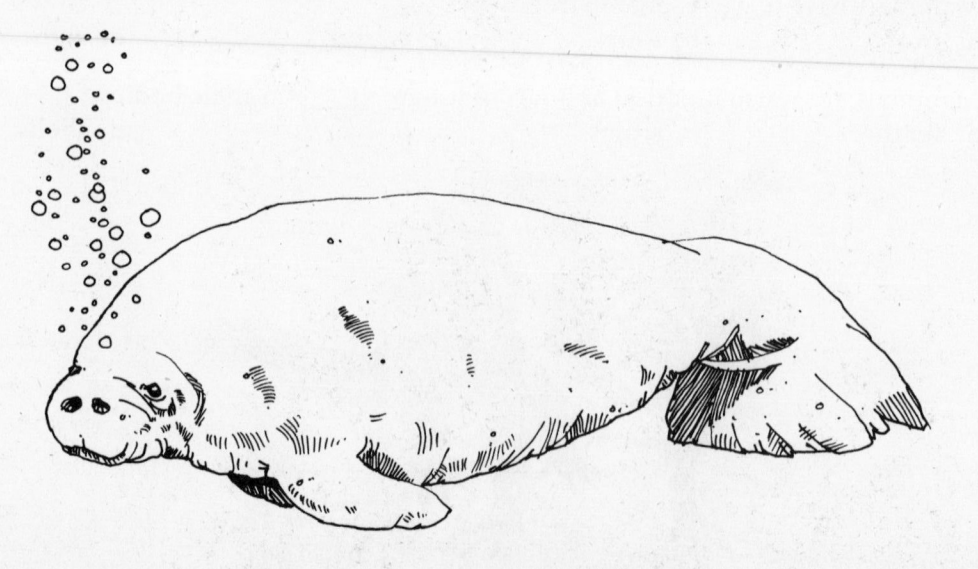

STUDY GUIDE

Types of Behavior

Use the clues to complete the puzzle.

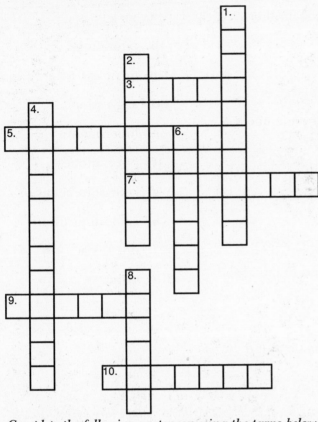

Across

3. behavior that is modified by experience is called trial and _____
5. something inside an animal that causes it to act; necessary for learning to occur
7. complex pattern of innate behavior, often having several parts
9. behavior that an organism is born with and which doesn't have to be learned
10. behavior that develops through experience

Down

1. a type of learning in which an animal forms a bond to another organism shortly after birth or hatching
2. the way an organism acts toward its environment
4. behavior that is modified so that a response becomes associated with another stimulus
6. a form of reasoning that allows animals to use past experiences to solve new problems
8. an automatic response that does not involve the brain

Complete the following sentences using the terms below.

trial and error	conditioning	imprinting	reflex	learn
recognition	motivation	stimulus	instinct	

1. Mating behavior of the male stickleback fish is an example of _____ .

2. Shivering is a _____ behavior.

3. Anything in the environment to which an organism responds is called a _____ .

4. Older quail will not crouch if a leaf falls because of their ability to _____ .

5. Imprinting is a learning pattern involving _____ .

6. Pavlov's dogs secreted saliva when a bell was rung even when no food was present because of

    _____ .

7. A hungry rat will be able to learn a maze if it receives food at the end. This is an example of

    _____ .

8. Riding a skateboard is learned by _____ .

9. Wolfgang Kohler's experiment showed that chimpanzees used _____ when they piled up boxes in order to reach bananas.

STUDY GUIDE

Behavioral Adaptations

Match the definitions on the left with the terms on the right by writing the correct letter in the space provided.

_____ **1.** a forceful act used to dominate or control another animal

_____ **2.** an exchange of information

_____ **3.** an instinctive seasonal movement of animals

_____ **4.** an area that an animal defends from other members of its species

_____ **5.** animals that are active during the night

_____ **6.** a group of animals of the same species that live and work together in an organized way

_____ **7.** attracts male moths from several kilometers away

_____ **8.** a cyclic response to cold temperatures and limited food supplies

_____ **9.** used to mark territories by cats and dogs

_____ **10.** allows males and females to be ready to mate at the same time

a. society

b. migration

c. territory

d. aggression

e. hibernation

f. pheromones

g. courtship behavior

h. communication

i. nocturnal

j. urine

Place a check (✓) next to the sentences that agree with the textbook. Rewrite the others so that they agree.

_____ **1.** Cyclic behaviors are learned by trial and error.

_____ **2.** An estivating animal becomes inactive and its metabolism slows down.

_____ **3.** Territories may be designated for one purpose such as feeding.

_____ **4.** Animals usually fight members of their own species to the death.

_____ **5.** Bright colors in birds are often designed to attract a mate.

_____ **6.** The dominant male controls the mating of females in a wolf pack.

_____ **7.** Pheromones are a form of communication.

_____ **8.** Crickets make sounds to warn others away from their territory.

_____ **9.** Animals that are inactive in the daytime are hibernating.

_____ **10.** Migration occurs in groups as a learned behavior.

STUDY GUIDE   Chapter 17

Rehabilitation of Wild Animals   Text Pages 406–407

Place a check (✓) next to the sentences that agree with the textbook. Rewrite the others so that they agree.

_____ 1. Once an injured animal has been restored to health, it always survives in its natural environment.

_____ 2. Natural selection is the process that occurs when the genes of weak individuals are removed from the population to insure the good health of future generations.

_____ 3. Wild animals are easy to care for.

_____ 4. Many animals are killed due to the movement of humans into animal territories.

_____ 5. If an owl is released in an area that has only enough resources for the one owl that already lives there, the newly released owl may not survive.

_____ 6. Electrical towers pose no danger to flying birds.

_____ 7. It is important to let injured birds of prey become accustomed gradually to humans.

_____ 8. Wildlife rehabilitation has become more popular in the United States.

_____ 9. The amount of food and shelter needed by animals in a given environment is called the carrying capacity.

_____ 10. If a rehabilitated wild animal does not survive after being released, the most likely cause is lack of resources.

Fill in the blanks with appropriate words from the textbook.

1. _____ cause millions of animals to be killed each year.

2. Wild animals are sometimes fed in captivity by _____ that look much like their natural parents.

3. The process of _____ results in removing the genes of weak individuals from the population.

4. Many _____ are electrocuted on telephone and electrical wires.

5. Reintroduction of rehabilitated animals can hurt _____ .

STUDY GUIDE

The Skeletal System

Write the letter of the term or phrase that best completes each statement.

_____ **1.** The tight-fitting membrane that covers bone is called _____ .
    a. osteoclast   **b.** marrow   **c.** periosteum   **d.** cartilage

_____ **2.** Any place where two or more bones meet is a(n) _____ .
    a. ligament   **b.** joint   **c.** osteoblast   **d.** fracture

_____ **3.** All the bones together make up the _____ .
    a. osteoclasts   **b.** skeletal system   **c.** immovable joint   **d.** periosteum

_____ **4.** Bones are held together by tough bands of tissue called _____ .
    a. cartilage   **b.** joints   **c.** ligaments   **d.** marrow

_____ **5.** The ends of bones at movable joints are covered with _____ .
    a. cartilage   **b.** ligaments   **c.** osteoclasts   **d.** periosteum

_____ **6.** A break in a bone is a(n) _____ .
    a. movable joint   **b.** periosteum   **c.** osteoblast   **d.** fracture

_____ **7.** The cavities in the center of large bones are filled with a fatty tissue called _____ .
    a. marrow   **b.** periosteum   **c.** cartilage   **d.** ligaments

_____ **8.** Where bones meet but there is little or no movement is a(n) _____ .
    a. hinge joint   **b.** immovable joint   **c.** gliding joint   **d.** pivot joint

_____ **9.** A type of bone cell called an _____ breaks down bone cells.
    a. osteoblast   **b.** immovable joint   **c.** elastic fiber   **d.** osteoclast

_____ **10.** Bone-forming cells are called _____ .
    a. osteoblasts   **b.** cartilage   **c.** osteoclasts   **d.** marrow

Name the four kinds of movable joints.

11. _____   **13.** _____

12. _____   **14.** _____

Label the two kinds of fractures shown below.

NAME _____ DATE _____ CLASS _____

STUDY GUIDE

The Muscular System

Check (✓) the statements that agree with the textbook. Rewrite the other statements so that they agree.

_____ 1. Skeletal muscles are attached to bones by tendons.

_____ 2. You have over 600 muscles in your body.

_____ 3. Smooth muscles are voluntary muscles.

_____ 4. How large a muscle becomes does not depend on how much work it does.

_____ 5. A muscle is an organ that contracts and gets shorter.

_____ 6. Cardiac muscle is only found in the heart.

_____ 7. Muscles never push; they always pull.

_____ 8. Muscles need large amounts of proteins to work well.

_____ 9. You don't need to think about how to control involuntary muscles.

_____ 10. Muscles use chemical energy in the form of glucose.

Label the following illustrations with one of the three types of muscles.

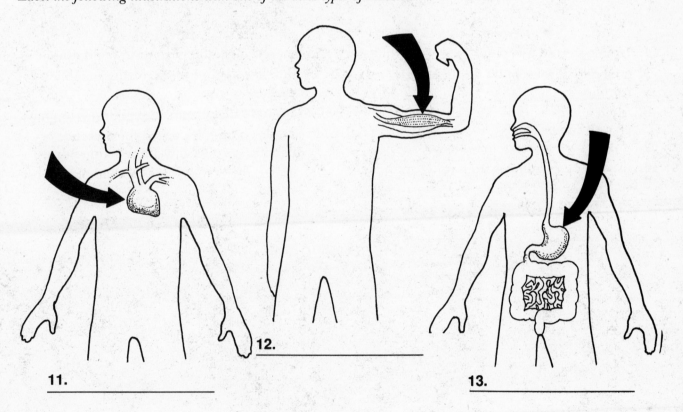

11. _____

12. _____

13. _____

STUDY GUIDE

Drugs for Fitness?

Use the clues to complete the puzzle.

Across

1. female steroid users may grow _____ hair
5. anabolic steroids build up these with exercise
8. when adolescents use steroids, their growth can be _____
9. muscles are made of this
10. used to deter athletes from using anabolic steroids

Down

2. may use anabolic steroids to build muscle
3. athletic competition that bans anabolic steroids
4. hormone that occurs in high levels in males
6. samples of this are tested for presence of anabolic steroids and other banned drugs
7. banned drugs that some football players use

STUDY GUIDE

Skin

*Cross out the statements that **DO NOT** agree with the textbook.*

1. Pigment cells are in the dermis layer of the skin.

2. There are only three sweat glands in the body.

3. Skin is the largest organ of the body.

4. The dermis is the layer of tissue under the epidermis.

5. The skin regulates body temperature.

6. Small amounts of vitamin D are produced in the epidermis in the presence of sunlight.

7. Melanin functions as a kind of sweat gland.

8. Skin is often 1 meter thick.

9. The epidermis is the surface layer of skin.

10. Thousands of your skin cells rub off every time you take a shower.

11. The more melanin you produce, the darker the color of your skin.

12. No nerve endings are in the skin.

13. The integumentary system includes the eyes and ears.

14. Skin excretes wastes from the body.

15. Skin serves as a protective covering for the body.

Label the two layers of skin in the diagram below.

16. _____

17. _____

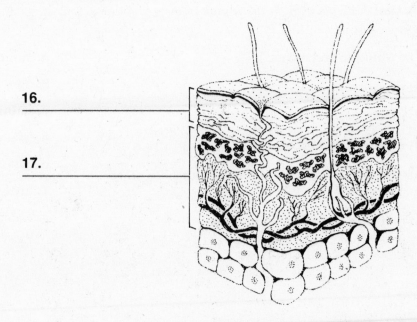

STUDY GUIDE

Nutrition

Check (✓) the statements that agree with the textbook.

_____ 1. The human body makes vitamin D when the skin is exposed to sunlight.

_____ 2. Nutrients provide energy and materials for cell development, growth, and repair.

_____ 3. The human body is 90 percent water.

_____ 4. The human body cannot construct essential amino acids inside body cells.

_____ 5. Starch, cellulose, and sugar are three types of carbohydrates.

_____ 6. Vitamins are organic nutrients that help the body use other nutrients.

_____ 7. Protein molecules are made up of amino acids.

_____ 8. Minerals are inorganic nutrients that regulate many chemical reactions in the body.

_____ 9. Unsaturated fats and saturated fats are types of minerals.

_____ 10. Carbohydrates are the main source of energy for your body.

_____ 11. Scurvy is a disease caused by a lack of vitamin K.

_____ 12. Minerals and water can be absorbed directly into the bloodstream.

_____ 13. Calcium, potassium, and sodium are minerals needed by the human body.

_____ 14. The four food groups are: minerals, carbohydrates, vitamins, and proteins.

_____ 15. The body loses about two liters of water every day through excretion, perspiration, and respiration.

Match the term in the second column with the description in the first column. Some items in the second column may not be used.

_____ 1. type of fat found in red meats

_____ 2. nutrient provided by citrus fruits

_____ 3. subunits of a molecule of protein

_____ 4. nutrient needed for good eyesight and healthy skin

_____ 5. nutrients that provide energy and help your body store some vitamins

_____ 6. nutrient that carries oxygen in the blood

a. amino acids

b. fats

c. saturated

d. vitamin C

e. vitamin A

f. iron

g. calcium

STUDY GUIDE

Chapter 19

Your Digestive System

Text Pages 451–455

Write the letter of the term or phrase that best completes each statement.

_____ 1. After being in the stomach for about four hours, food has been changed to a liquid
called _____ .
    a. amylase   **b.** chyme

_____ 2. Chewing food in the mouth is an example of _____ .
    a. mechanical digestion   **b.** chemical digestion

_____ 3. The gall bladder produces a greenish fluid called _____ .
    a. bile   **b.** feces

_____ 4. The _____ absorbs large amounts of water from undigested food.
    a. small intestine   **b.** large intestine

_____ 5. Muscular waves or contractions that move food are called _____ .
    a. homeostasis   **b.** peristalsis

_____ 6. The process that breaks down food so that it can be taken into the cells is called _____ .
    a. peristalsis   **b.** digestion

_____ 7. Glands in your mouth produce _____ .
    a. saliva   **b.** chyme

_____ 8. The breakdown of large molecules into smaller ones to be absorbed by the cells is called
_____ .
    a. chemical digestion   **b.** mechanical digestion

_____ 9. _____ that live in the large intestine feed on undigested material.
    a. Bacteria   **b.** Viruses

_____ 10. Saliva contains the enzyme _____ .
    a. chyme   **b.** amylase

The following are the major organs of the digestive system. Rewrite them in the order in which food passes through them.

large intestine   anus   mouth   stomach
small intestine   esophagus   rectum

1. _____

2. _____

3. _____

4. _____

5. _____

6. _____

7. _____

STUDY GUIDE

Eating Disorders
Text Pages 456–457

*Cross out the statements that **DO NOT** agree with the textbook.*

1. We often rely on food to make us feel better.

2. Anorexia nervosa and bulimia can damage the heart.

3. In anorexia nervosa, basic nutritional needs of the body are not satisfied.

4. An eating disorder can be corrected easily.

5. Boys never get eating disorders such as bulimia.

6. Anorexia nervosa is an eating disorder that involves extreme weight loss.

7. Bulimics never exercise.

8. Anorexia nervosa is an eating disorder that causes a person to eat too much.

9. Bulimia involves binge eating, followed by self-induced vomiting.

10. The lack of food in anorexia nervosa causes starvation-like symptoms, such as general weakness and loss of bone mass.

11. The person who is bulimic almost always gets over this disorder without any outside help.

12. Constant vomiting can result in damage to the teeth.

13. Both anorexia nervosa and bulimia can result in death.

14. A person with anorexia nervosa often uses laxatives.

15. Extreme weight loss and self-induced vomiting make a person less attractive.

STUDY GUIDE
Chapter 20

Circulation
Text Pages 464–470

Fill in the blanks with the correct terms.

1. High blood pressure, or _____ is a common disorder that can be caused by clogged arteries.

2. Arteries may be clogged by fatty deposits on their walls, causing the condition known as _____ .

3. The blood vessels that move blood away from the heart are called _____ .

4. The microscopic blood vessels that connect arteries and veins are called _____ .

5. The blood vessels that carry blood toward the heart are called _____ .

6. Blood from all parts of the body, except the lungs, goes to the _____ of the heart .

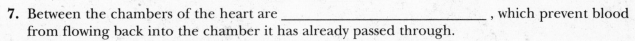

7. Between the chambers of the heart are _____ , which prevent blood from flowing back into the chamber it has already passed through.

8. The rate at which your heart beats is set by the _____ . It does this by signaling the right atrium to contract.

9. Blood moves from the right atrium to the _____ .

10. The tissue that divides the right and left sides of the heart is called the _____ .

11. From the right ventricle, blood moves to the _____ .

12. The flow of blood through the heart, to the lungs, and back to the heart is called _____ .

13. Oxygen-rich blood moves through the pulmonary vein from the lungs to the _____ .

14. Blood moves from the _____ to most parts of the body.

15. The _____ moves blood to all body tissues except the lungs and heart.

16. The _____ is the flow of blood to the tissues of the heart.

STUDY GUIDE

Blood

Answer the following questions.

1. What percentage of your body mass is blood? _____

2. What is blood made of? _____

3. What is plasma made of? _____

4. Which gas does blood carry to cells of the body? What else does it carry to the cells?

   _____

5. Which gas does blood carry away from cells of the body? What else does it carry away from the

   cells?_____

6. Which type of blood cells are more numerous in the blood? _____

7. What type of blood cells fight infection? _____

8. What blood type contains both substance A and substance B? _____

9. What blood type contains neither substance A nor substance B? _____

10. How long do red blood cells live? _____ How long do white blood

    cells live? _____

Use terms from your textbook to complete the sentences below.

11. Red blood cells carry _____ , a chemical that can pick up oxygen and
    carbon dioxide.

12. A person receives blood or blood parts during a _____ .

13. A disease in which one or more types of white blood cells are produced in greater number is

    called _____ .

14. A disorder in which there are few red blood cells or too little hemoglobin in the blood is called

    _____ .

15. The liquid part of blood that is mostly made of water is called _____ .

16. The odd-shaped cell fragments that help clot blood are called _____ .

17. _____ fight bacteria, viruses, and other foreign substances in the body.

18. Blood groups and _____ are checked before transfusions are given.

19. Your body reacts to infection by _____ its white blood count.

STUDY GUIDE

Chapter 20

Autologous Blood Transfusions

Text Pages 478–479

Answer the following questions.

1. What is the difference between an autologous and a homologous blood transfer?

_____

_____

_____

2. When might a person choose to have blood taken for an autologous blood transfusion?

_____

3. Give two advantages of an autologous blood transfusion over a homologous blood transfusion.

_____

_____

_____

4. Why is an autologous blood transfusion like "money in the bank"? _____

_____

_____

5. What are two disadvantages for storing your blood for an autologous blood transfusion some

time in the future? _____

_____

_____

6. Describe how blood "lost" in surgery can be reused. _____

_____

_____

7. When might the use of artificial hemoglobin be helpful? _____

_____

_____

8. In addition to artificial hemoglobin, what other discoveries may be helpful in avoiding homolo-

gous blood transfers? Explain how they would be helpful. _____

_____

_____

STUDY GUIDE

Your Lymphatic System

Use terms from the textbook to fill in the blanks below.

1. A soft mass of tissue that produces lymphocytes is the _____ .

2. Microorganisms and foreign materials are filtered out of the lymph in the

_____ .

3. The system that collects fluid from body tissue spaces and returns the fluid to the blood is

called the _____ .

4. Fluid found outside body cells is called _____ .

5. The organ that filters bacteria, foreign particles, and damaged red blood cells out of the blood

is the _____ .

6. White blood cells that fight infection are called _____ .

Mark each of the following statements true or false. If a statement is false, change the underlined term to make the statement true.

7. A person with AIDS is <u>able</u> to fight infections of the body due to the number of T cells present.

_____

8. Bacteria and other foreign materials are filtered out of the blood by the <u>lymph nodes</u>.

_____

9. Like <u>arteries,</u> the lymphatic vessels have valves that prevent the backward flow of fluid.

_____

10. If <u>lymph</u> were not carried away from tissues of the body by the lymphatic system, the tissues

would swell and eventually burst. _____

11. The <u>thymus</u> protects the mouth and nose from infection. _____

12. The lymph is made up of water, dissolved substances, and <u>lymphocytes.</u> _____

13. <u>After</u> lymph enters blood, it is filtered in structures called lymph nodes.

_____

14. The thymus produces <u>red</u> blood cells. _____

15. Unlike the <u>circulatory system</u>, the lymphatic system has no structure to pump the fluid

through the body. _____

16. AIDS is a virus that destroys <u>all</u> lymphocytes. _____

17. The <u>circulatory</u> system helps the body fight infection. _____

STUDY GUIDE

Your Respiratory System

Study the diagram below. Then label each of the numbered structures.

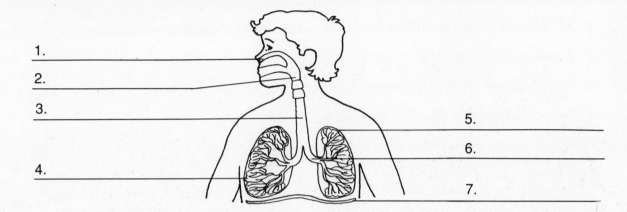

1. _____

2. _____

3. _____

4. _____

5. _____

6. _____

7. _____

Fill in the blank with the term that best completes each sentence.

8. The smallest tubes in the lungs are the _____ .

9. The _____ prevents food from entering the trachea.

10. The pharynx is a passageway for _____ and _____ .

11. The alveoli are surrounded by _____ .

12. Air entering your body is first moistened and warmed in the _____ .

13. The trachea is kept open by rings made of _____ .

Place a check (✔) beside the sentences that agree with the textbook. Rewrite the others so that they agree.

_____ 14. Emphysema can result in the blood being low in hemoglobin.

_____ 15. The greatest contributing factor to lung cancer is inhaling the tar in cigarette smoke.

_____ 16. People who produce too much mucus in the bronchial tubes have a disease called emphysema.

_____ 17. A lung disorder often associated with allergies is called asthma.

_____ 18. The diaphragm is a muscle beneath the lungs.

_____ 19. The mucus lining the trachea moves foreign particles to the esophagus.

_____ 20. When you inhale, your diaphragm relaxes.

STUDY GUIDE

Dangerous Breathing

Place a check (✓) beside the sentences that agree with the textbook. Rewrite the other sentences so that they agree.

_____ 1. As a result of exercise, the lungs can hold greater quantities of air.

_____ 2. As the body perspires, fluids come to the skin's surface causing overheating.

_____ 3. Exercising near polluted air can be dangerous.

_____ 4. Sulfur dioxide is found in cigarette smoke.

_____ 5. Nitrogen dioxide is found in farm silos.

_____ 6. Rats that exercised after being exposed to nitrogen dioxide suffered no more lung damage than rats that weren't exercised.

_____ 7. Research has shown that the amount of nitrogen dioxide that causes lung damage in rats is only half the amount a typical smoker inhales from one puff of a cigarette.

_____ 8. Miners should avoid strenuous labor after exposure to high nitrogen dioxide levels.

_____ 9. As a result of exercise, it is easier to breathe because the lungs are capable of taking up more carbon dioxide and removing more oxygen from the blood.

_____ 10. Nitrogen dioxide is found in automobile exhaust.

Complete the crossword puzzle below using words from the textbook.

Across

1. _____ can cause high blood pressure .
6. As a result of exercise, lungs can hold more _____ .
7. Muscle tone is improved by regular _____ .
8. _____ cools skin during exercise.
10. Emphysema causes _____ damage.
11. Perspiration removes dirt from pores in the _____ .

Down

2. These chemicals are harmful to health.
3. Lungs remove _____ dioxide from the blood.
4. Firemen are at risk because of exposure to heavy _____ .
5. _____ dioxide is found in cigarette smoke.
9. Nitrogen dioxide is found in farm _____ .

STUDY GUIDE

Your Urinary System

Fill in the blank with the term that best completes each sentence.

1. The organs of the urinary system help control blood _____ by removing excess water.

2. Capillaries coming from the tubules in the kidneys merge to form small

   _____ .

3. In the nephron, water, sugar, and salt are reabsorbed by _____ surrounding the tubule.

4. Perspiration contains water and _____ .

5. Your urinary system helps your body maintain _____ with the help of other excretory organs.

6. Waste products that are not removed can accumulate and act as

   _____ .

7. Urine in each _____ drains into a funnel-shaped area of each kidney that leads to the ureters.

8. The process of artificially filtering blood is called _____ .

9. The lungs are also _____ organs because they remove carbon dioxide and water.

10. An adult can lose about _____ liter(s) of water through urine each day.

Write the letter of the correct word in the blank next to each description.

_____ 11. the filtering units in the kidney

_____ 12. leads from the bladder to outside the body

_____ 13. returns purified blood to the body from the kidneys

_____ 14. tubes leading from each kidney to the bladder

_____ 15. contains blood entering the kidneys

_____ 16. muscular organ that holds urine

_____ 17. kidneys, lungs, and skin are all _____ organs

_____ 18. creates fog when you breathe on a cold window

_____ 19. lungs excrete water and _____

_____ 20. blood is pumped through this during dialysis

a. excretory

b. ureters

c. bladder

d. urethra

e. carbon dioxide

f. moisture (water)

g. nephrons

h. renal veins

i. aorta

j. permeable tubing

STUDY GUIDE

Your Nervous System

Write the letter of the term or phrase that best completes each sentence.

_____ 1. The small space between one neuron and the next is called a(n) _____ .
   a. dendrite   b. synapse   c. axon   d. interneuron

_____ 2. The working unit of the nervous system is the _____ .
   a. axon   b. reflex   c. brainstem   d. neuron

_____ 3. An automatic response to a stimulus is called a _____ .
   a. reflex   b. neuron   c. synapse   d. nerve

_____ 4. The branch of the neuron cell body that receives messages is called a _____ .
   a. dendrite   b. neuron   c. synapse   d. reflex

_____ 5. _____ send impulses to the brain.
   a. Motor neurons   c. Interneurons
   b. Sensory neurons   d. Reflexes

_____ 6. The cranial nerves and the spinal nerves make up the _____ nervous system.
   a. central   b. cranial   c. peripheral   d. sensory

_____ 7. _____ conduct impulses from the brain to muscles or glands.
   a. Sensory neurons   c. Motor neurons
   b. Interneurons   d. Reflexes

_____ 8. The _____ is the extension of the neuron cell body that carries away messages.
   a. dendrite   b. axon   c. synapse   d. interneuron

_____ 9. The brain and spinal cord make up the _____ nervous system.
   a. central   b. somatic   c. peripheral   d. autonomic

_____ 10. Small nerve cells throughout the brain and spinal cord are called _____ .
   a. motor neurons   c. sensory neurons
   b. dendrites   d. interneurons

Label the three parts of the brain in the diagram below.

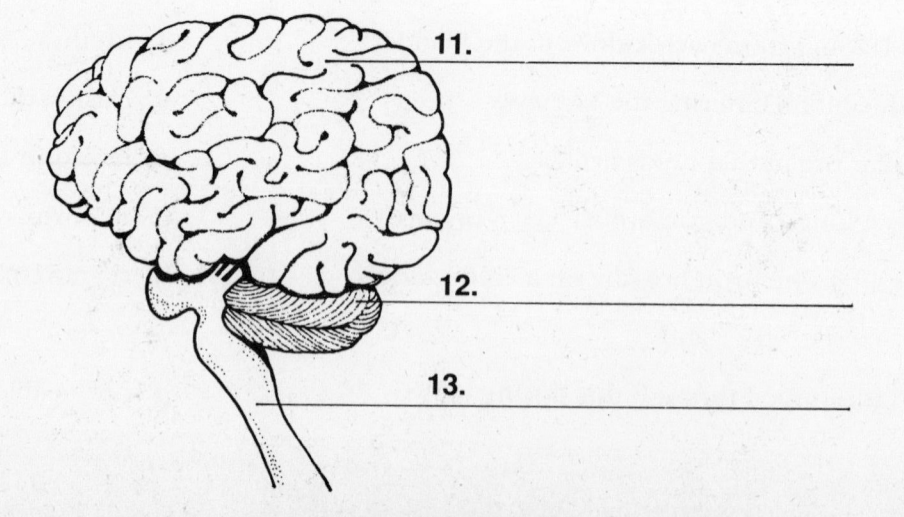

11. _____

12. _____

13. _____

STUDY GUIDE

The Senses

*Cross out the statements that **DO NOT** agree with the textbook.*

1. The olfactory cells are kept moist by mucous glands.

2. Your eyes are equipped with structures to bend and focus light.

3. Hearing in no way depends on impulses from nerves.

4. The tissue at the back of the eye that is sensitive to light energy is called the retina.

5. An impulse from the olfactory cells travels first to the spinal cord.

6. Taste and odor have nothing to do with each other.

7. The fluid-filled structure shaped like a snail's shell in the inner ear is called the cochlea.

8. The lens of the eye focuses the light rays onto the retina.

9. The auditory nerve sends impulses concerning taste to your brain.

10. Taste buds respond to four basic taste sensations.

Label the three main sections of the ear.

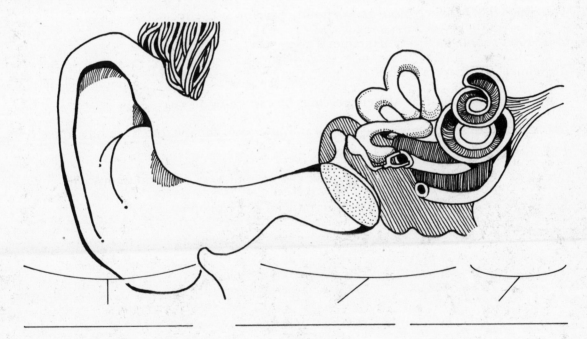

STUDY GUIDE

Alzheimer's Disease

*Cross out the statements that **DO NOT** agree with the textbook.*

1. Children of Alzheimer's victims have a 50 percent chance of getting the disease later in life.

2. Without acetylcholine, nerve impulses are not carried from one neuron to the next.

3. The cost of keeping someone in a nursing home averages about $25 000 a year.

4. Alzheimer's disease is harmful but no one dies from it.

5. The cure for Alzheimer's disease has just been found.

6. Alzheimer's disease is a failure of nerve cells in the brain to communicate with one another.

7. Some researchers think that a defect in chromosome 19 can cause Alzheimer's disease.

8. Alzheimer's victims lose muscle control but retain good memory.

9. Alzheimer's disease definitely has no genetic cause.

10. Alzheimer's disease causes severe memory loss.

11. Caregivers of Alzheimer's victims often suffer from the stress of the situation.

12. The drugs that produce more acetylcholine have no side effects.

13. Only 1000 people die from Alzheimer's every year.

14. Alzheimer's destroys brain cells.

15. Some scientists think that Alzheimer's may be caused by a virus.

16. In patients with Alzheimer's, the chemical that crosses the synapse from one nerve cell to another is present.

17. Over a period of years, victims of Alzheimer's become very different people.

18. The protein, amyloid B, may work differently in older people.

NAME _____ DATE _____ CLASS _____

STUDY GUIDE

Your Endocrine System

Check (✔) the statements that agree with the textbook.

_____ 1. Diabetics are people who make too much insulin.

_____ 2. The endocrine system consists of ductless glands throughout the body.

_____ 3. Target tissues are frequently close to the gland that affects them.

_____ 4. An adrenal gland is located at the top of each kidney.

_____ 5. Endocrine secretions are called hormones.

_____ 6. To control the amount of hormone an endocrine gland produces, the body has a negative feedback system.

_____ 7. Endocrine glands produce substances that flow through ducts.

_____ 8. There is only one adrenal gland.

_____ 9. The specific tissues that hormones affect are called target tissues.

_____ 10. The pituitary gland is located at the base of the brain.

_____ 11. The parathyroid glands are located on the pancreas.

_____ 12. Insulin enables cell membranes to take in glucose.

_____ 13. The thyroid gland is located on the trachea.

_____ 14. The islets of Langerhans are part of the kidneys.

_____ 15. Hormones move directly from the gland into the bloodstream.

Match the description in the first column with the gland in the second column.

_____ 16. keeps calcium and phosphorous at a steady level in the blood

_____ 17. regulates the rate at which energy is used by cells

_____ 18. enables cell membranes to take in glucose

_____ 19. controls other endocrine glands in the body

_____ 20. causes blood vessels to expand in emergency situations

a. islets of Langerhans

b. parathyroid

c. adrenal

d. pituitary

e. thyroid

STUDY GUIDE

Human Reproduction

Complete the following sentences using appropriate terms from the textbook.

1. The _____ helps regulate body temperature for sperm production.

2. The production of eggs and sperm begins during _____.

3. Sperm is produced in the _____.

4. The urethra is a passageway for urine as well as for _____.

5. Egg cells are produced in the _____.

6. Fertilization usually takes place in the _____.

7. The menstrual cycle is controlled by _____ from the pituitary gland.

8. There is a reduction in _____ and _____ as menopause approaches.

9. The head of a sperm contains _____.

10. The gland that produces a nourishing fluid for sperm is called the _____.

Complete the crossword puzzle below using terms from the textbook.

Across
1. monthly discharge of uterine lining and blood
4. monthly cycle in female that is controlled by hormones produced in the pituitary gland and the ovaries
6. female reproductive cells
8. male reproductive cells
9. mixture of sperm and fluid

Down
1. menstrual cycle becomes irregular and stops
2. pear-shaped muscular organ in which a baby develops
3. produce sperm
5. female organs that produce eggs
7. passageway from the uterus to the outside of a female's body

STUDY GUIDE   Chapter 23

Fertilization to Birth   Text Pages 535–539

Place a check (✓) next to the statements below that agree with the textbook. Rewrite the other statements so that they agree.

_____ **1.** A human zygote has 46 chromosomes.

_____ **2.** During the first two months of pregnancy, the unborn child is called a fetus.

_____ **3.** The amniotic sac helps cushion the baby.

_____ **4.** Wastes are carried through arteries in the umbilical cord.

_____ **5.** Blood vessels develop from the villi to form the placenta.

_____ **-6.** The heart begins to beat in the first three months of development.

_____ **7.** If two eggs are fertilized at the same time, identical twins result.

_____ **8.** The amniotic sac attaches to the placenta.

_____ **9.** More than one sperm can fertilize a single egg.

_____ **10.** The fetus often sucks its thumb while in the uterus.

Match the description in the first column with the item in the second column by writing the correct letter in the space provided.

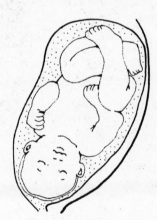

_____ **11.** contains the chromosomes in both sperm and egg

_____ **12.** the process that occurs when egg and sperm unite

_____ **13.** twins that come from a single egg

_____ **14.** filled with fluid that cushions the baby while inside the uterus

_____ **15.** transports nutrients and oxygen to the baby

_____ **16.** refers to the developing baby after the first two months of pregnancy

_____ **17.** twins that come from two eggs

_____ **18.** refers to the developing baby during the first two months of pregnancy

_____ **19.** formed by the union of egg and sperm

_____ **20.** place where the fertilized egg implants

a. fraternal

b. uterus

c. fertilization

d. umbilical cord

e. amniotic sac

f. embryo

g. zygote

h. fetus

i. identical

j. nucleus

STUDY GUIDE

Development After Birth

Match the description in the first column with the item in the second column by writing the correct letter in the space provided.

_____ 1. surgery performed when a baby cannot be born through the vagina

_____ 2. muscular contractions of the uterus that begin childbirth

_____ 3. expelled by contractions after the baby is delivered

_____ 4. refers to the first four weeks after birth

_____ 5. hormone that helps produce reproductive cells

_____ 6. the scar that forms where the umbilical cord was attached to the baby

_____ 7. early contractions often cause it to break and release its fluid

_____ 8. begins from ages 12 to 14

_____ 9. period of development from 1 to 12 years

_____ 10. period from 4 weeks to 1 year

a. FSH

b. adolescence

c. neonatal period

d. cesarean section

e. childhood

f. labor

g. infancy

h. navel

i. amniotic sac

j. placenta

Number these developmental events (1-7) in the order that they normally occur.

_____ Child sits up when propped.

_____ Child can walk without help.

_____ Child says simple words such as "mama."

_____ Many can read a limited number of words.

_____ Child can control bladder and bowel.

_____ Child can smile.

_____ Child can speak in simple sentences.

STUDY GUIDE
Chapter 23

Aging
Text Pages 544–545

Place a check (✓) next to the statements that agree with the textbook. Rewrite the others so that they agree.

_____ **1.** The cost of health care in the United States has been gradually declining.

_____ **2.** Arthritis is a disease associated with aging.

_____ **3.** Within 60 years, nearly a fourth of the population will be age 65 and older.

_____ **4.** Researchers have found that stress reduction is not a factor in promoting health.

_____ **5.** Hydrogen peroxide causes cellular destruction.

_____ **6.** Genes appear to play a role in the aging process.

_____ **7.** It is possible to avoid the aging process by developing healthful habits.

_____ **8.** When catalase production is increased, cellular damage is reduced in fruit flies.

_____ **9.** The harmful effects of aging can be reversed in humans by causing the gene for catalase production to be overexpressed.

_____ **10.** Toward the end of a normal life, the immune system deteriorates and nerves degenerate.

Complete the following sentences using the terms below.

gene	enzyme	hydrogen peroxide
overexpressed	catalase	aging

11. The substance that breaks down hydrogen peroxide is called _____.

12. Catalase is an _____ .

13. The action of _____ causes damage to cells, which may play a role in

_____ .

14. If the _____ for catalase can be _____ , a
greater amount of hydrogen peroxide would be broken down.

91

STUDY GUIDE

The Nature of Disease

Complete the crossword puzzle using words from the textbook.

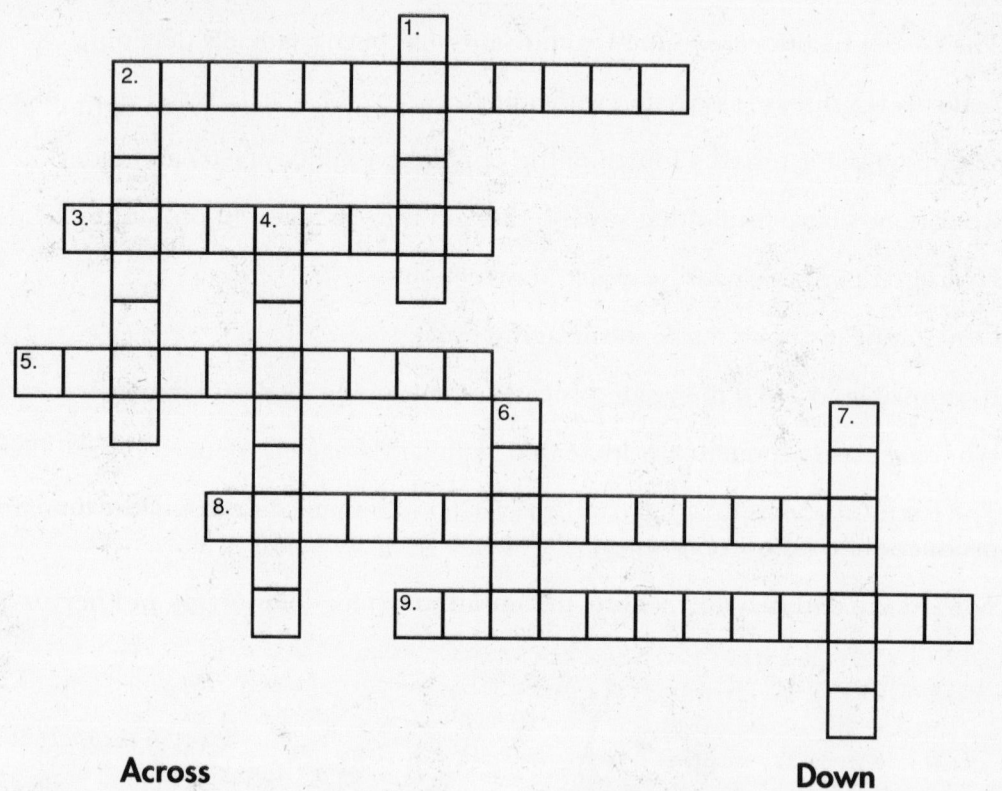

Across

2. a disease that is spread or transmitted from one organism to another

3. a sexually transmitted disease caused by bacteria

5. antibiotic used to treat syphilis

8. process of heating food to a temperature that kills most bacteria

9. kills pathogens on nonliving objects

Down

1. English surgeon who recognized the need for cleanliness in surgery

2. added to swimming pools and city water systems to kill pathogens

4. in some persons the organism that causes syphilis has become _____ to penicillin

6. particles spread by sneezing

7. cold viruses can be spread by _____

Complete the following sentences using appropriate terms from the textbook.

1. The AIDS virus can pass through the _____ and infect an unborn child.

2. Pathogens on the skin can be killed by washing with _____ soaps.

3. Most diseases are caused by viruses and harmful bacteria known as _____ .

4. According to Koch's rules, when pathogens from a pure culture are injected into a test animal,

they must cause the _____ disease.

5. Some of the most dangerous diseases are spread by _____ contact.

6. STDs that are caused by _____ can be treated with antibiotics.

7. If left untreated, gonorrhea or chlamydia can cause _____ .

STUDY GUIDE

Chapter 24

Your Immune System

Text Pages 563–566

Place a check (✔) next to the sentences that agree with the textbook. Rewrite the others so that they agree.

_____ 1. An antibody attaches to an antigen to make it harmless.

_____ 2. Your body has a complex group of defenses called lymphocytes to fight disease.

_____ 3. White blood cells sweep up and digest bacteria that get into the body.

_____ 4. A vaccine gives you active immunity without having to get the disease.

_____ 5. Most bacteria cause disease.

_____ 6. Passive immunity does not last as long as active immunity.

_____ 7. Sulfuric acid in the stomach kills bacteria that enter your body on the food you eat.

_____ 8. People with AIDS usually die from other diseases because the AIDS virus destroys lymphocytes, leaving the person's body defenseless.

_____ 9. When the body is invaded by a pathogen, it starts to make antigens.

_____ 10. Fever generally helps to fight pathogens.

Match the statement on the left with the term on the right by writing the correct letter in the space provided.

_____ 11. virus that destroys the immune system

_____ 12. disease-causing bacteria

_____ 13. traps pathogens in nasal passage

_____ 14. proteins and chemicals that are foreign to the body

_____ 15. made from weakened or killed pathogens

_____ 16. immunity occurring when your body makes its own antibodies

_____ 17. substance made in response to an antigen

_____ 18. immunity occurring when antibodies are introduced from an outside source

_____ 19. cells attacked by AIDS virus

_____ 20. destroy pathogens in mouth, stomach, pancreas, and liver

a. active

b. antigens

c. passive

d. mucus

e. lymphocytes

f. antibody

g. enzymes

h. pathogens

i. vaccine

j. AIDS

STUDY GUIDE

Chapter 24

Preventing Disease

Text Pages 568–569

Match the statement on the left with the term on the right by writing the correct letter in the space provided.

_____ 1. needed when one dose of vaccine doesn't provide long-lasting protection

_____ 2. developed by Salk and Sabin

_____ 3. often developed by people with AIDS

_____ 4. time when vaccines against mumps, measles, tetanus, whooping cough, and polio should be given

_____ 5. time when a second vaccination is recommended

_____ 6. virus that damages the immune system

_____ 7. developed the first vaccine

_____ 8. a weakened virus that allows you to develop immunity against a disease

_____ 9. disease eliminated by Jenner's vaccine

_____ 10. show whether you have been vaccinated

a. tuberculosis

b. vaccine

c. polio vaccine

d. Edward Jenner

e. smallpox

f. booster shot

g. AIDS

h. medical records

i. 15 months

j. 6th or 7th grade

Place a check (✓) next to the sentences that agree with the textbook. Rewrite the others so that they agree.

_____ 11. Jonas Salk and Carl Sabin invented the first vaccine.

_____ 12. Measles and mumps are beginning to reappear in the United States.

_____ 13. Adults must remember to get booster shots for tetanus.

_____ 14. All babies are currently being vaccinated against mumps, measles, tetanus, whooping cough, and polio.

_____ 15. Cleanliness, eating right, and getting plenty of rest and exercise are some of the ways you can prevent disease.

_____ 16. Over 20 000 new cases of whooping cough are being reported each year.

_____ 17. A vaccine may be injected or swallowed.

_____ 18. Those who work or live with people infected with tuberculosis stand the chance of developing AIDS.

_____ 19. Tuberculosis has returned in part because people with AIDS are unable to fight off the infection, and often develop the disease.

_____ 20. Doctors do not recommend getting a second vaccination.

STUDY GUIDE
Chapter 24

Noncommunicable Disease
Text Pages 570–573

Complete the following crossword puzzle using appropriate terms from the textbook.

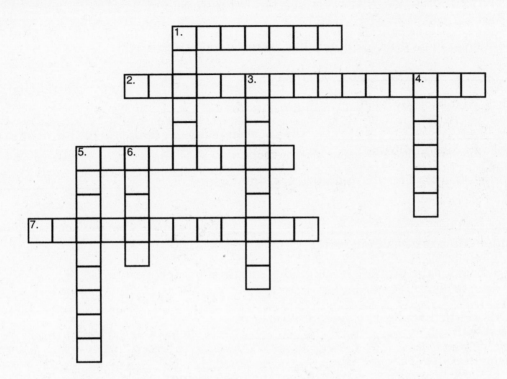

Across
1. diseases that last a long time
2. diseases that are not spread from one person to another
5. chronic disease in which antibodies are made against proteins in the joints
7. use of chemicals to destroy cancer cells

Down
1. results from uncontrolled cell growth
3. tumor that is cancerous and can spread
4. tumor that is not cancerous
5. substances that cause an allergic response
6. any abnormal growth

Place a check (✓) next to the sentences that agree with the textbook. Rewrite the others so that they agree.

_____ 1. Allergic reactions can be severe enough to cause death if not treated promptly.

_____ 2. Arthritis results from a faulty immune system.

_____ 3. Most cancers are characterized by uncontrolled cell growth.

_____ 4. All tumors are cancerous.

_____ 5. Some allergies can be treated by injecting small doses of antibodies.

STUDY GUIDE

Drugs and Health

Complete the following sentences using the appropriate words from the textbook.

1. A person who has _____ really believes that he or she needs the drug.

2. Deliberately using a drug for other than its intended purpose is

   _____ .

3. The drug in tobacco is called _____ .

4. In _____ , the sugar in fruits or grains reacts with yeast to produce alcohol and carbon dioxide.

5. Heavy use of alcohol results in destruction and change of _____ cells.

6. An illness called _____ occurs when a person who is physically dependent on a drug cannot get that drug.

7. Using a drug for the purpose it was made, but using it improperly is called

   _____ .

8. A person with _____ has a chemical need for a drug.

9. The drug in coffee, caffeine, is a _____ .

10. _____ is when a body adjusts to a drug, and larger doses of the drug are needed to achieve the same effect.

11. Alcohol slows down the central nervous system and therefore is a

    _____ .

In the blank at the left, write the letter of the term or phrase that best completes each sentence.

_____ 12. Nicotine is the drug found in _____ .
   a. tobacco   b. alcohol

_____ 13. Passive smoke contains _____ tar, nicotine, and carbon monoxide than the smoke inhaled by the smoker.
   a. more   b. less

_____ 14. When alcohol enters the bloodstream, it goes to _____ .
   a. only the brain   b. all body tissues

_____ 15. Drinking alcohol actually _____ the body.
   a. warms   b. cools

_____ 16. Alcohol causes the drinker to have a _____ reaction time.
   a. slower   b. faster

STUDY GUIDE

Drugs in Society

Check (✔) the statements that agree with the textbook.

_____ **1.** The United States' war on drugs has had little impact on the problem of drug abuse.

_____ **2.** Methamphetamine slows down the body.

_____ **3.** More drugs are entering the United States than ever before.

_____ **4.** Violence is currently America's greatest concern.

_____ **5.** Babies born to mothers who abuse drugs do not suffer the effects of the drugs.

_____ **6.** Educating the general public about the effects of drugs is one effort of the war on drugs.

_____ **7.** Industrial accidents can result from drug abuse.

_____ **8.** The 60 to 70 percent increase in the prices of some drugs on the streets reflects increased availability.

_____ **9.** The United States has strengthened law enforcement in an attempt to fight the war on drugs.

_____ **10.** Drug abuse has no real effect on the business world.

_____ **11.** The effects of methamphetamine last up to two hours.

_____ **12.** When a manufacturer loses money due to drug abuse, consumers may pay higher prices for products.

_____ **13.** The United States has increased military forces to try to keep drugs out of the country.

_____ **14.** In the business world, drug abuse never results in loss of productivity.

_____ **15.** About 520 000 acres of land are currently used to grow the coca plant in North America.

_____ **16.** Addicts have been unable to produce a synthetic cocaine.

_____ **17.** Crank is another name for methamphetamine.

_____ **18.** The drug abuse problem in the U.S. is close to being solved.

_____ **19.** Absenteeism and lateness, resulting from drug abuse, are problems for businesses.

_____ **20.** Everyone is affected by the problem of drug abuse in America.

STUDY GUIDE

Problems with Illegal Drugs

Text Pages 588–593

*Cross out the statements that **DO NOT** agree with the textbook.*

1. Cocaine was once an ingredient in many over-the-counter drugs.
2. Barbiturates slow down the cardiovascular and respiratory systems.
3. Crack is a smokable form of opium.
4. Marijuana is made from the hemp plant.
5. A person quickly gets AIDS if they use LSD.
6. Marijuana causes physical dependence.
7. A hallucinogen affects a user's perception and consciousness about the world around him or her.
8. An overdose of depressants can cause coma, depressed breathing, uncontrolled muscle spasms, and eventually death.
9. Amphetamines are a group of stimulants.
10. Hashish is a form of crack.
11. Heroin is one of the most addictive drugs.
12. Morphine was used as a pain killer in the Civil War.
13. The use of marijuana increases a person's reaction time.
14. Use of crack can cause heart failure.
15. The Pure Food and Drug Act required that medicine labels indicate the presence of alcohol, opium, or morphine.

Use the clues below to complete the puzzle.

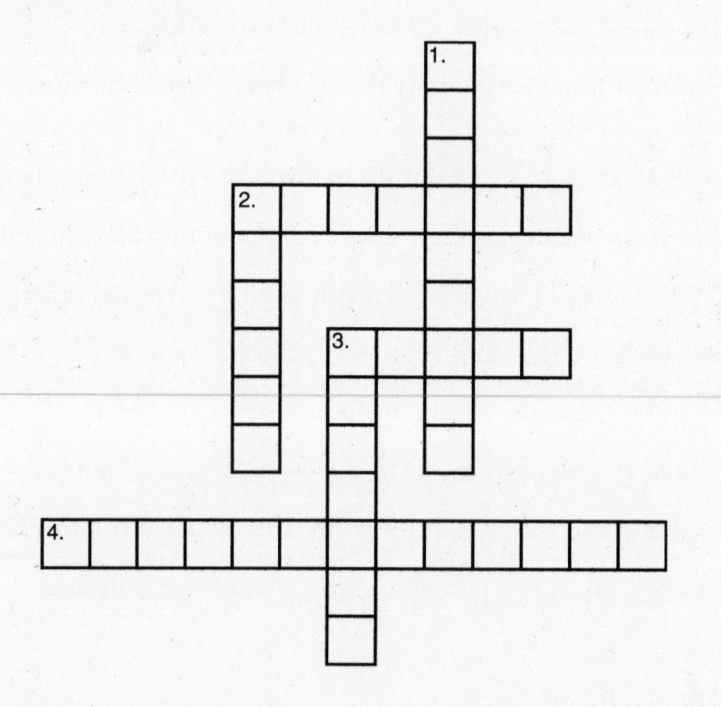

Across

2. made from flowering top of Indian hemp
3. a smokable form of cocaine
4. illegal drugs that affect users' perception

Down

1. also called "pot"
2. made from morphine
3. an illegal drug made from coca leaves

STUDY GUIDE
Chapter 26

Organisms and Their Environments
Text Pages 606–611

Write the letter of the term or phrase that best completes each sentence.

_____ 1. The population _____ is the number of individuals per unit of living space.
    a. biosphere   **b.** density   **c.** community   **d.** spacing

_____ 2. Nonliving things in the environment are _____ factors.
    a. abiotic   **b.** population   **c.** biotic   **d.** mineral

_____ 3. The _____ species is more abundant than others in the community.
    a. niche   **b.** dominant   **c.** biotic   **d.** coral

_____ 4. The biosphere includes all the air, land, and water where _____ exists.
    a. an abiotic factor   **b.** coral   **c.** life   **d.** a niche

_____ 5. In an ecosystem, a community interacts with the _____ factors of the environment.
    a. biotic   **b.** abiotic   **c.** chemical   **d.** spacing

_____ 6. A community is made up of _____ .
    a. environments   **b.** niches   **c.** factors   **d.** populations

_____ 7. The _____ of a population changes as new individuals are born and old ones die.
    a. spacing   **b.** niche   **c.** density   **d.** size

_____ 8. For a coral reef, the ocean water is a(n) _____ .
    a. abiotic factor   **b.** niche   **c.** biotic factor   **d.** community

_____ 9. Living things in the environment are _____ factors.
    a. abiotic   **b.** density   **c.** biotic   **d.** community

Complete the following sentences using the appropriate terms from the textbook.

10. All the parts of Earth where life is found make up the _____ .

11. The organisms of one species living together in the same place at the same time form

    a(n) _____ .

12. How individuals are arranged in an area is called _____ .

13. All the populations in the same place at the same time make up a(n) _____ .

14. The role of a species within a community is its _____ .

15. The place where an organism lives in a community is its _____ .

16. Population density is determined by dividing the _____ by the number of individuals of an area.

17. A community interacting with the abiotic parts of its environment is

    a(n) _____ .

STUDY GUIDE   Chapter 26

Biotic Relationships   Text Pages 612–616

*Cross out the statements that **DO NOT** agree with the textbook.*

1. Competition can occur between members of the same species.

2. Producers are the first link in a food chain.

3. No energy is lost in an energy pyramid as it moves toward the top.

4. A food web is a series of overlapping food chains.

5. A mouse is a consumer of foxes for food.

6. Competition always occurs when several species live near each other.

7. In some food webs, consumers eat both plants and animals.

8. Animals at the top of food chains depend on large populations to stay alive.

9. A symbiotic relationship is when two or more species live together.

10. Mutualistic relationships occur when plants compete with animals.

11. An owl eating a sparrow is an example of a predator-prey relationship.

12. The flow of energy in an energy pyramid is from the bottom to the top.

Complete the following sentences using the appropriate terms from the textbook.

13. In _____ , an animal copies the appearance or behavior of another organism.

14. A tree frog hides from predators by using _____ .

15. In the relationship known as _____ , the host is harmed.

16. A series of overlapping food chains is called a(n) _____ .

17. _____ determines the size and location of populations.

18. In _____ , both members of a symbiotic relationship benefit.

19. In a(n) _____ , less energy is available at the top.

20. The following series of illustrations is an example of a(n) _____ .

STUDY GUIDE

Abiotic Factors in the Biosphere

Check (✓) the statements that agree with the textbook.

_____ **1.** Organisms today are using the same materials that have been used since life began.

_____ **2.** Animals use carbon dioxide for respiration.

_____ **3.** Lightning changes a small amount of oxygen into nitrogen compounds.

_____ **4.** The sun's energy is needed for the water cycle.

_____ **5.** Plants absorb carbon dioxide during photosynthesis.

_____ **6.** Rain, snow, sleet, and hail are all forms of condensation.

_____ **7.** The last step of a cycle brings the process back to the starting point.

_____ **8.** Bacteria associated with plants convert nitrogen to usable nitrogen compounds.

_____ **9.** Decomposers break down carbon compounds in dead organisms and release carbon dioxide into the air.

_____ **10.** Nitrogen is the only element needed by living things that is returned to the environment.

Label this diagram of the water cycle.

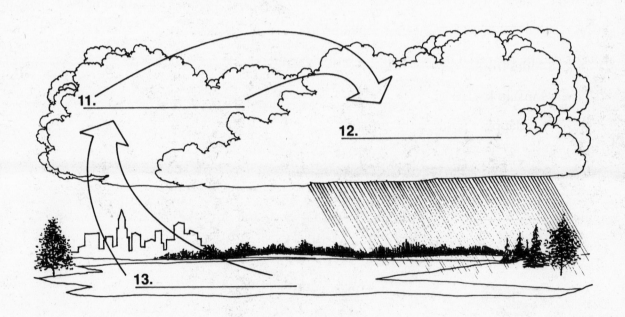

11. _____

12. _____

13. _____

STUDY GUIDE

Friendly Fires

*Cross out the statements that **DO NOT** agree with the textbook.*

1. Some forests require fires to maintain their character.

2. Forest fires always start with a strike of lightning.

3. Researchers think animals move away from fires and so are usually not harmed.

4. Controlled burns never cause any real harm.

5. Natural fires usually produce less heat than controlled burns.

6. Without natural fires, dead leaves and other material build up on the forest floor.

7. Controlled burns are managed forest fires that are set by biologists.

8. Sometimes the wind causes controlled fires to move in a direction not desired by the biologists.

9. Lodgepole pines have cones that don't open to release seeds until they have been heated in a fire.

10. Controlled fires eliminate eyesores for people who live near the forest.

11. Controlled fires never produce air pollution.

12. Controlled fires eliminate the fuel that might feed a large and uncontrolled natural fire.

13. The red-cockaded woodpecker depends on fires to keep hardwoods from growing in its habitat.

14. Local residents always like to see a controlled fire.

15. Forests can be damaged by both natural and controlled fires.

STUDY GUIDE

Factors that Affect Biomes

*Cross out the statements that **DO NOT** agree with the textbook.*

1. Sunlight can be a limiting factor for green plants.

2. Pine trees are the climax community in an oak-hickory forest.

3. Secondary succession occurred at Yellowstone National Park after the forest fires of 1988.

4. A desert can be a climax community.

5. After a volcanic eruption, pioneer species begin to break down the rock.

6. Secondary succession comes immediately after primary succession.

7. As long as environmental conditions remain the same, there can be no climax community.

8. Any factor that limits the number or distribution of organisms is a limiting factor.

9. Oak seedlings can grow in the shade.

10. Primary succession takes about 10 years to occur.

11. Pine forests can never be the final stage of succession.

12. A climax community is made up of organisms that are adapted to the climate and soil conditions of an area.

13. When a farmer abandons a pasture, the land begins the first stages of primary succession.

14. Each species has adapted to a set of biotic and abiotic factors in its environment.

15. Succession continues until the same species continuously grow and reproduce.

Complete the following sentences using the appropriate words from the textbook.

16. A community that is able to remain stable in an area is a _____ .

17. _____ is the development of new communities in newly created land areas.

18. A condition that determines the survival of an organism, population, or species in its environ-

    ment is a _____ .

19. _____ is the gradual change in a community over time.

20. _____ occurs when a disturbed area gradually returns to its previous condition.

STUDY GUIDE

Land Biomes

Write the letter of the term or phrase that best completes each sentence.

_____ **1.** Soil that is permanently frozen is called _____ .
    a. biome   **b.** tundra   **c.** icepack   **d.** permafrost

_____ **2.** The average weather in an area is called _____ .
    a. precipitation   **b.** climate   **c.** biomes   **d.** summer

_____ **3.** Evergreen trees are the dominant plants in a _____ biome.
    a. tundra   **b.** coniferous forest   **c.** deciduous forest   **d.** tropical rain forest

_____ **4.** A _____ biome is dominated by broad-leaved trees such as maples and hickories.
    a. coniferous forest **b.** tundra   **c.** deciduous forest   **d.** tropical rain forest

_____ **5.** Grasslands are called _____ in North America.
    a. deserts   **b.** prairies   **c.** biomes   **d.** forests

_____ **6.** Large geographical areas that have similar climates and climax communities are called
_____ .
    a. biomes   **b.** forests   **c.** countries   **d.** environments

_____ **7.** _____ are home to more than 50 percent of the species on Earth.
    a. Biomes   **c.** Tropical rain forests
    b. Deciduous forests   **d.** Grasslands

_____ **8.** A cold, treeless biome is the _____ .
    a. desert   **b.** permafrost   **c.** grassland   **d.** tundra

_____ **9.** A _____ biome has hot days and cold nights because of little cloud cover.
    a. coniferous forest **b.** tundra   **c.** desert   **d.** grassland

Identify the biome in which you would expect to find each of the following organisms by writing the biome name under each picture.

10. _____   **11.** _____   **12.** _____

13. _____   **14.** _____   **15.** _____

STUDY GUIDE

Water Ecosystems

Check (✔) the statements that agree with the textbook. Rewrite those that disagree.

_____ 1. Most life in the ocean is found in the littoral and sublittoral zones.

_____ 2. An estuary is the area where a freshwater river or stream meets the ocean.

_____ 3. Fast-moving streams contain large amounts of oxygen.

_____ 4. About a quarter of the world is covered by water today.

_____ 5. Organisms at the littoral zone have adapted to the constant temperature of that zone.

_____ 6. Life probably first arose in the oceans.

_____ 7. The marine ecosystem covers more than 70 percent of Earth's surface.

_____ 8. Fresh water contains about 3.5 percent salt.

_____ 9. Ponds that are cloudy or green contain very few nutrients.

_____ 10. Water temperature in freshwater ecosystems does not vary as much as the temperature of the air.

_____ 11. Because estuaries are so deep, light cannot penetrate to the bottom.

_____ 12. Lakes and ponds are classified according to the amount of organic matter they contain.

Label the diagram with the three major zones of the ocean.

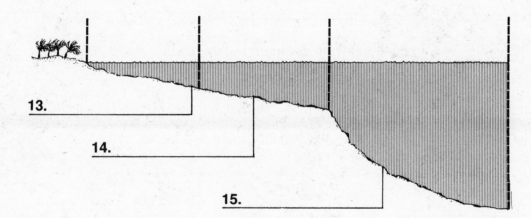

13. _____

14. _____

15. _____

STUDY GUIDE

Coastal Wetlands

*Cross out the statements that **DO NOT** agree with the textbook.*

1. Wetlands serve as filters to clean surface water.

2. Wetlands provide a resting and feeding place for migrating birds.

3. Wetlands are a cause of water pollution in many areas.

4. Wetlands are generally useless in economic terms.

5. The Great Lakes are our most important wetlands.

6. Many people think of wetlands as breeding grounds for mosquitoes.

7. Coastal wetland plants absorb many of the pollutants carried to the coast by rivers and streams.

8. Most humans rely on the water table for drinking water.

9. Millions of hectares of wetlands have been drained in the United States for development.

10. The lakes, rivers, and streams of America serve as its water table.

11. Rainwater helps clean polluted wetlands.

12. Many species of plants and animals are endangered because of the loss of wetlands.

13. A wetland is an area of land that for at least part of the year is covered by shallow water.

14. Animals visit but do not live in wetlands.

15. Wetlands along a coast are important in providing food and jobs for humans.

16. When it rains, rainwater soaks into the ground until it reaches the water table.

17. The increasing need to build homes and schools will eventually save many wetland areas.

18. Fish avoid wetlands because there is no food there.

19. About 90 percent of the fish harvested in the United States spend part of the year in wetlands.

20. Coastal marshes serve as protection against storms and floods.

Natural Resources

Write the letter of the term or phrase that best completes each sentence.

_____ 1. Loss of soil from the effects of wind, water, or ice is called _____ .
      a. land pollution   **b.** erosion

_____ 2. Fresh water accounts for about _____ percent of the total water on Earth.
      a. 3   **b.** 20

_____ 3. The unwanted products that are burned, buried, and dumped each year are
      called _____ .
      a. solid wastes   **b.** nonbiodegradable

_____ 4. Supplies of natural resources on Earth are _____ .
      a. unlimited   **b.** limited

_____ 5. Wastes that are _____ create pollution problems for years.
      a. unlimited   **b.** nonbiodegradable

_____ 6. Chemicals that are byproducts of industrial processes are called _____ .
      a. solid wastes   **b.** toxic wastes

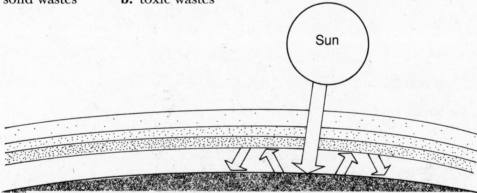

7. What does the illustration above represent? _____

8. What is a possible outcome of the process shown in the illustration? _____

_____

Complete the following sentences using the appropriate terms from the textbook.

9. Natural resources that can be replaced by nature over time are _____ .

10. Organisms that might become extinct are known as _____ .

11. The burning of _____ to produce electricity releases tons of sulfur
dioxide into the air each year.

12. Those natural resources that are available only in limited amounts are

called _____ .

13. Pesticides and fertilizers used on lawns and farms can cause _____ .

STUDY GUIDE

Conservation and Protection

Complete the following sentences using the appropriate terms from the textbook.

1. The process of replanting a cut-over area with seedling trees is called _____ .

2. Many communities _____ to reduce wastes and reuse precious natural resources.

3. _____ is the wise and careful use of Earth's resources.

4. An area of land set up to protect animal species is a _____ .

5. The Clean Air Act of 1990 required industries to reduce their _____ emissions by 40 percent by the year 2000.

6. What kind of power can be produced by harnessing the force shown in the illustration below?

   _____

*Cross out the statements that **DO NOT** agree with the textbook.*

7. Many countries protect forest resources by developing national parks and forests.

8. More than half of the endangered species worldwide are in the United States.

9. Reforestation causes erosion because the new roots disturb the soil of an area.

10. Modern windmills can generate hydroelectric power.

11. As the human population grows, there is less need to protect natural resources.

12. Water treatment plants kill bacteria and filter out sediments from a community's water supply.

13. Solar energy collected by solar panels during the day can be used to produce electricity at night.

14. The wild turkey that once was common in America now has become extinct.

15. Some cities have built trash-burning power plants that can produce electricity.

STUDY GUIDE   Chapter 28

Future Responsibility   Text Pages 658–659

Check (✔) the statements that agree with the textbook.

_____ 1. Whenever a development is planned, its effects on the environment must be considered.

_____ 2. Only human life depends on Earth's resources.

_____ 3. Pesticides destroy apples and other fruits.

_____ 4. Environmental management is using methods that conserve resources and protect eco-systems.

_____ 5. Changes made in the planning stages of developments can sometimes eliminate damage to the environment.

_____ 6. Volunteering your time to a conservation organization is one way to be environmentally responsible.

_____ 7. Compost piles help recycle glass and aluminum.

_____ 8. Turning off lights will not save natural resources.

_____ 9. Every person in a community has a responsibility to the environment.

_____ 10. When the Alaska pipeline was built, the environmental hazards had to be weighed against the benefits of the pipeline.

_____ 11. Good planning will always eliminate damage to the environment.

_____ 12. Pesticides cause wormholes.

_____ 13. With so many people on Earth, natural resources and ecosystems are under a lot of pressure.

_____ 14. Spraying pesticides on trees prevents damage from pests.

_____ 15. Oil, paint, and batteries should be disposed of properly.

STUDY GUIDE

Earth in 2030

*Cross out the statements that **DO NOT** agree with the textbook.*

1. No one should worry about the future because the outlook is good.

2. Environmental activists work to conserve Earth's resources and to protect the environment.

3. Plastic containers could be used to make building materials.

4. The population of Earth nearly doubled between 1960 and 1990.

5. Walking or biking instead of traveling by car will protect the environment.

6. Coal, oil, and natural gas will always be our main sources of energy.

7. Environmental activists have a negative effect on Earth.

8. Recycling is not practical for industry.

9. People in the United States are throwing away 160 million tons of solid waste every year.

10. Pollutants in the air are causing global warming and acid rain.

11. In the future, many people will communicate with the office by computer or telephone.

12. Deforestation will definitely be stopped in the year 2000.

13. Solar energy and wind and water power could become the main sources of electricity in the future.

14. Everyone should be thinking about the environment for future generations.

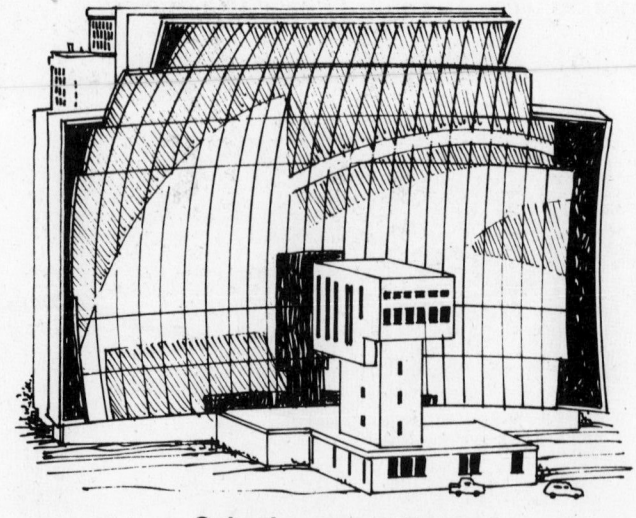

Solar furnace in France